™

Deadlands Dime Novel #9

Fiction & Adventure by: Lester Smith

Editing & Layout: Barry Doyle, Hal Mangold &
Charles Ryan
Cover Art: Kevin Sharpe with Matt Tice
Logo: Ron Spencer
Interior Art: Chris Musto
Cover Design: Hal Mangold & Matt Tice
Map: Barry Doyle

Pinnacle Entertainment Group, Inc.
P.O. Box 10908
Blacksburg, VA 24062-0908
www.peginc.com or deadlands@aol.com
(800) 214-5645 (orders only)

Visit our website at **www.peginc.com** for regular free updates.

Deadlands: The Weird West created by Shane Lacy Hensley.

™

SKINNERS

PROLOGUE

He stalked forward through the mist, the loose gravel crunching beneath the weight of his feet. It was difficult enough to see in the dim moonlight, and the thick fog in the air didn't help any.

"Damn peculiar," he thought. He couldn't remember how he got here, or where here was. Something wasn't right, and he had a feeling in his gut that he'd find out what was happening soon enough.

A breeze picked up, and the mists began to shift and swirl, making weird patterns in the air. He could occasionally hear a strange sound over the wind and rocks crunching under his feet. It sounded like chanting.

Ronan continued forward, his hand on his shooting iron, ready if he needed it. The mists parted slightly, and the chanting grew louder. He was able to make out trees all around him, their branches barren of their leaves.

The trees weren't completely bare, however. There were bodies hanging from them, swaying in the breeze. The branches creaked and moaned with their weight.

Ronan had seen many a man hang in his time, but this was different. The men seemed more like linens hanging from a wash line. The scene was surrealistic.

As Ronan closed in on one of the trees, something fell from above and draped over his head and shoulders. He pulled the leathery sheet from his head as fast as he could, and looked to see what it was.

"Son-of-a...!," he shouted. It was a skin, a man's skin! "What the Hell is going on here?" he yelled into the mists, and he threw the skin to the ground.

The wind began to pick up a little, and the shamans chant faded with it. A woman's laugh began to fill the air. It was a sinister, sick laugh.

The skins on the trees began to moan and howl as the wind rushed into them and out of their mouths and eyes. Ronan grew more and more agitated.

"What the Hell is this place?" he growled. "Am I finally dead? Are you finally gonna let me move on, or is this another one of your tricks, demon? Answer me!"

The laughter grew louder, and a figure moved in the mists. He drew his pistol and cocked it, pointing it at the moving shape.

"Show yourself, demon! I'm ready to throw down!"

The laughter grew to an unbearable level, and the silhouette moved towards Ronan. It glided over the ground, seemingly floating with the fog.

As it closed in on Ronan, he could see that the ghostly figure was wrapped in animal skins. It had its arm raised, and it carried a huge, stone dagger that dripped with blood.

Ronan fired at the spectre, pumping slug after slug into it. Its laugh changed to a high pitched scream, and it pressed on towards the gunslinger, unaffected by his attack.

Ronan couldn't stop it! It enfolded him, and the scream filled his ears like the whine of a steam whistle...

CHAPTER ONE

The woman's scream shocked Ronan Lynch awake. He was on his feet, Colt Peacemaker in hand, almost before his eyes had fully opened. A quick glance around the lounge revealed no danger, however. He realized he was having a nightmare, and the woman's scream wasn't from the ghostly spectre in his vision.

The other riverboat passengers seemed as startled as he was. It was difficult to tell, though, if it was more from the scream or the sight of this rangy cowboy on his feet with drawn gun.

Groggily, Ronan shook his head, then listened again. There was a babble of panicked voices from outside, apparently on the dock. Spinning his Colt once in his hand, he headed for the door.

A young, pimpled steward tried to intercept him.

"Excuse me, sir," the young man stammered. "You really should remain on board. I'm sure the captain has whatever it is under control."

Ronan glowered down at the young man. Out West, stepping into another man's path was an invitation for a gunfight, and Ronan already had his hogleg in his hand.

Still, he figured, New Orleans was a slightly more civilized locale, and the steward was just trying to do his job. On the other hand, he was irritated at being startled awake, and he wanted to go see what was causing all the fuss. So he glared a little harder at the fellow, and let just a hint of hellish light glint within his eyes. The steward paled, gulped and took a seat. Ronan stomped through the door and out onto the main deck of the *Marie Belle*, one of the most elegant riverboats to ply the Mississippi.

Immediately, he regretted the impulse that had led him to frighten the steward. Sure, he had managed to avoid an argument with the steward, but at what cost? That was the trouble with being dead and reanimated by some sort of demon. It was constantly a battle for control. So the demon found little ways to make its presence known. Ways like playing upon Ronan's irritation at the young steward, and prompting that little light show with the eyes. Ronan hoped that he would just put it down to a trick of the light, or his own imagination.

Ronan strode across the deck, heading for the dock. It was still dark out; the sun hadn't yet risen, though the eastern sky was beginning to pale. Far behind the undead cowboy, it revealed the silhouette of New Orleans on the opposite bank of the great Mississippi. On the near side of the river, the warehouses of Algiers bulked darkly, blocking the view beyond.

Down on the dock, a crowd was gathered. As Ronan strode down the gangplank he noted a few late passengers clustered in the lamplight at its foot. They were gathered around the prone figure of a short young woman, apparently unconscious, her flouncy skirts in disarray, revealing a plumply fetching calf and dainty ankle. Beyond that group, a larger band of dock workers and ship's crew, many carrying lanterns and torches, were gathered around something else lying on the dock. From the expressions on their faces, whatever it was sure wasn't pretty. One burly laborer in that group suddenly broke away and vomited his breakfast into the river. Seconds later, another man decided to join him.

Ronan spared one glance for the young woman as he passed. The *Marie Belle's* chief steward, Simms, a slight man in his thirties, knelt beside her with a vial of smelling salts. Already she was coming around, choking on the fumes. The cowboy moved on.

Ronan shouldered his way through the cluster of dock workers. Captain Manning and his first mate were at the center. The captain was shouting for people to back off and make room. His weathered face had an unhealthy red cast in the light of the torches, and his white hair and beard stood out starkly against his dark cap and coat. The pilot, McCombs, was drawing a tarp over a shape lying on the planks.

"You there!" Captain Manning lit an eye on one of the dock workers. "You look like you might have a lick of sense, unlike the rest of these rummies. Run back into town and fetch the police. Tell them there's been a murder."

Ronan crouched and lifted a corner of the tarp. Underneath lay a naked human figure, dripping river water and blood onto the planks. The corpse was more than naked; Ronan realized suddenly that the figure had no skin. The body had been flayed, leaving muscle, tendon, and bone nakedly visible from head to foot. He dropped the tarp again, and stood up with a grim expression wrinkling his face.

Captain Manning laid a hand on Ronan's shoulder. "Not a pretty sight, is it, my friend?" he said, swallowing nervously. "I know you've seen a lot of weird stuff in your travels. But have you ever seen anything like this before," he asked.

Ronan looked him in the eye and shook his head. "Nope," he said. "This is a new one even on me, pardner."

He squared his shoulders, shaking off the memory of the sight beneath the tarp.

"Well, is there some way I can help?" he asked.

"How about taking a look around before absolutely all the clues have been trampled?" the captain suggested. "We've taken a quick look, but another eye wouldn't hurt at all."

Glancing around at the clustered bystanders, Ronan calmly drew his pistol and fired a round into the air. That got their attention. As the echoes died among the stacked crates along the dock, he took a deep breath.

"All right, show's over," he growled. "Everybody get back to work, or move along and let the captain and his crew do their jobs."

The crowd began dispersing.

Ronan took the mate's lantern. He lifted it high and peered around the dock nearby. A trail of bloodstained water ran from the body to the nearest edge of the dock. A length of wet rope lay in an untidy pile nearby. It was darkly stained in spots near one end, and looked to have fragments of flesh ground into some of the rough fibers.

"One of the dock workers spotted the body floating in the river," Captain Manning volunteered. He swallowed uncomfortably. "The fellow thought it was someone drowning. He jumped in to help, and a friend tossed down the rope.

"In the darkness, they didn't realize its 'condition.' But when they hauled it up into the light..." Manning's voice trailed off as he thought about the gruesome sight again.

"And that's when the woman came along," Ronan suggested.

Manning nodded grimly. "Yeah. Bad timing, huh?" He sort of coughed a laugh.

"Sorry," he drew himself up. "It's just so..."

SKINNERS

"Yeah, it is." Ronan said. "Well, whoever he was, he's still bleedin' all over creation. He can't have been in the water long. Anybody see or hear anything before the body was spotted?"

"No. We asked. Whoever killed him did it very quietly." He gestured toward the first mate. "I sent McCombs here down onto the bank under the dock to take a look around, and he found the spot where it must have happened. There are a few marks of a scuffle, and a lot of spilled blood."

"Sounds 'bout right," Ronan said. "The muscles of his throat are cut. Must have been taken from behind. Kinda makes a man wonder what he was doing down there in the first place?"

The captain rubbed an unsteady hand along his bearded jaw. "It might help if we knew who the blazes he is."

Ronan sighed and gave a nod. "But how do you identify a flayed corpse? And where the Hell is his skin now?

The cowboy went to take a look at the scuffed ground under the docks. There weren't many clues to be found. The bank was pebbled, so it didn't hold footprints, though there were a few scars where it seemed that feet had dug in for purchase during a struggle. The lantern also revealed a wide, sticky splash of blood across the pebbles, just now beginning to dry. Once the sun rose, the spot would be swarming with flies, he figured.

Ronan looked up the slope, deeper under the dock. The pilings gave ample hiding places for a dozen men. The murderer could easily have waited for his victim's back to be turned, then stepped forward and cut the throat from behind. But why had his victim come down here in the first place? And why kill him? Worse, why skin him afterward?

The more the gunslinger thought about it, the skinning just didn't make sense. But Ronan knew there were a lot of other things in the world that didn't make sense nowadays. Like ghost rock, vampires riding trains, and undead cowboys too cussed to give in to the demon writhing inside them.

So now there was another monster loose in the world, one that killed and then skinned its victims. It was a mystery, but most mysteries had a way of revealing themselves if they were looked into hard enough. With that in mind, he clambered back up onto the dock.

CHAPTER TWO

Detective Matthews took one look under the tarp and swore. He dropped it quickly and backed away. The sun had risen, and with the growing warmth flies were swarming around the tarp.

The detective took a few calming breaths, then started asking questions. He received the same answers Ronan had. He went to look at the scuffmarks in the bank, but they didn't reveal anything he didn't already know.

He questioned everyone on the dock as to his or her whereabouts and actions since first thing this morning. Finally, he accompanied Captain Manning aboard the *Marie Belle*, to talk in the pilothouse at its top, where they could have some privacy. The captain invited Ronan along.

"He's an old friend, and one heckuva man" Captain Manning explained, "He might be able to lend a helping hand."

The detective didn't object, though he did give the cowboy a long, measuring look.

The pilothouse lent a good view of the surrounding area. It was glassed in, front and back, so the pilot could watch the river for signs of snags and sandbars during a voyage. Once the ship was underway, an officer and a steersman would man the wheelhouse just below. With the ship tied up at dock, however, the captain sent everyone away, so that he and Lynch could talk with the lawman in private.

"So, no skin, no clothing, no nothing," Matthews said. "They didn't leave anything for us to identify the body."

"Maybe that was their purpose," Captain Manning suggested.

"Seems an awful lot of trouble just to make him anonymous," Matthews replied. "Considering that people were coming and going on the dock above, I don't think I'd have taken the time if I were the killer."

Ronan nodded. "Yeah. There has to be some reason for taking the skin. At one time, I'd have said it was some sorta revenge."

"But now?" Matthews turned a sharp eye in the cowboy's direction.

"Never mind, pardner," Ronan answered. "Let's just say I've seen enough to stop making guesses. I've learned to just keep my eyes open, and my hand on the grips."

Matthews considered this for a moment, then said, "Well, considering the circumstances, I think it would be best if the *Marie Belle's* voyage were delayed until we can get some answers."

Captain Manning groaned. "The owners are going to have my hide," he said. "If the boat doesn't sail, they don't make money. And they hate losing out on money."

"Murder does have a way of inconveniencing us all," the detective wryly replied, then added, by way of concession, "We'll just have to hope we can get the investigation wrapped up quickly, and get you on your way."

Ronan snorted.

The detective shot him a dirty look.

"Well, we'd best go talk to your passengers, Captain," Ronan said, pretending to ignore Matthews. "Why don't you lead the way, lawman."

Manning sighed, then opened the port side door and gestured them through.

*　　　*　　　*

The chief steward gathered all the passengers and crew together in the central dining room, at the captain's request. Morning sun brightly lit the huge chamber. Spotless white linen tablecloths fairly glowed in the light, and even the dark wood paneling of the walls glistened with polish. The chandelier had been lit as well, dispelling shadows along the balcony and even on the high ceiling. But it was a gloomy group that watched the captain, detective, and cowboy enter.

"Good morning, everyone," Detective Matthews began. "I appreciate your patience with the situation we find ourselves facing. For those of you who haven't yet heard, there was a murder near the docks this morning. We found a dead man with no skin," he said, boldly.

Ronan scanned the group for reactions.

The ship stewards, nattily dressed in white serving jackets and black trousers, stood at attention near the door leading to the aft lounge. Simms, the Chief Steward, an unobtrusive fellow of medium height, weight, and age, outwardly appeared unfazed by the news, but Ronan noted that his normally warm eyes looked troubled.

The two stewards, both in their early twenties, one short, portly, and pimpled (the young man Ronan had stared down earlier), and the other thin and balding prematurely, both let out a shocked gasp. But Simms glared at them, and they quickly regained their composure.

At a table nearby, a fat, blustery little middle-aged man in an expensive suit chewed the end of a cigar. This was Senator Milton Howard, Ronan recalled, remembering the passenger descriptions that the captain had given him earlier in the day. He watched the fellow's face take on a calculating expression.

Likely the senator was wondering what effect this news was going to have on his "pressing schedule." At the senator's side sat a redheaded, freckled young man in a similar, though obviously less expensive suit. This would be Jefferson Andrews, Ronan thought.

Ironically, Andrews' face bore the evidence of far more intelligence than the senator whom he assisted. At the moment, however, he looked grim. Perhaps he knew or suspected something about the victim. Ronan made a mental note to quiz Andrews thoroughly when the opportunity presented itself, but now wasn't the time.

Seated on a bench behind the senator's table was a young couple the passenger list identified as Jack and Rita Baroni. They were newlyweds, as evidenced by the way in which Rita clutched at Jack's arm. She was a short, slightly plump little creature with curly blond hair and gray eyes.

Ronan recognized her as the woman who had fainted on the dock. Right now, her dainty face looked pale, her eyes wide. Likely she'd be having nightmares about that sight for years to come, Ronan thought, shaking his head slightly.

For his part, Jack seemed made of sterner stuff. Slim and good-looking, with thick, curly black hair and cornflower blue eyes, he hid his reaction to the news well. Or perhaps he was simply too unimaginative to have been moved by it. Ronan couldn't decide.

At another table, closer to the front of the room, a thin, pale woman of advanced age sat stiffly, an expression of outraged disapproval animating her wrinkled features. Her age-spotted hands clenched and unclenched angrily on the head of a walking cane. This would be Adelia MacPherson, Ronan realized, a wealthy dowager who had outlived three husbands. He imagined her discovering the murderer and thrashing him with that cane. The thought drew a grim smile across his lips.

To her left stood a tall, bony man who had to be her son. The family resemblance was strong. Randall, his name was, a bachelor who devoted his life to caring for his aged mother. At first glance, he seemed entirely overshadowed by his domineering parent. But Ronan noted a levelness to his gaze that bespoke a stubborn patience in its own right. No telling what might be going on in this one's head, no matter how dutiful he might seem.

Lounging near a window behind the dowager and her son stood a slickly handsome man gone slightly to seed with middle age. His curly black hair had grayed at the temples, his blue eyes had yellowed slightly around the edges, and his lean, muscular figure was beginning to stretch the waist of his black vest just a bit. He toyed nervously with a deck of cards while trying to feign a helpful interest in the proceedings.

Ronan noted a shot glass on the windowsill at the man's elbow. The sun hadn't been up long, but this man was drinking hard stuff already. Carmichael was his name, Rusty Carmichael. The captain had pointed it out on the manifest, explaining "He makes his living playing cards, fleecing the foolish, but he always pays his ticket in advance, so there's not much I can say about it." Ronan wondered if a riverboat gambler might have a reason for killing and skinning a man.

A quiet young woman with a fetching figure, a pretty face, and soft brown hair and eyes sat at the piano to the right of the forward door. Alice Monroe was her name. Catching Ronan's eye on her, she smiled warmly. It wasn't an entirely innocent smile. She was sizing the cowboy up, and apparently she liked what she saw. Ronan nodded politely, if a trifle coolly. Ronan had learned it was better that way, since there was no telling what the demon thing inside him might do.

At a table alone in the middle of the room sat an American Indian, dressed up like a dude in a brown serge suit and a derby hat. His arms were crossed on his chest, and his face betrayed no emotion, though his eyes scanned everyone in the room, as watchful as Ronan's own. "Tom Black Eagle" he had signed the book. Ronan knew how savage many tribes could be toward whites. It was quite possible that Black Eagle was the very man the detective sought.

Finally, there were eight crewman seated in a cluster at a table to Ronan's left: Four bosuns, and four engineers, two each for each six-hour shift. Half of them looked a bit groggy, the off-duty group. Captain Manning had sworn by them all as men he knew and trusted. He'd also pointed out that working in shifts as they did, none was ever far from at least one of the others, so unless at least two of them were in on it together, none of them could have committed the murder. Ronan suspected that the captain was correct, but he planned to speak to the men nonetheless.

Ronan turned his attention back to Detective Matthews, who had finished explaining the state in which the body had been found.

"Given the seriousness of the act," Matthews was saying, "I see no recourse but to hold the *Marie Belle* here in New Orleans until the investigation has been concluded." He opened his mouth to speak further, but was interrupted by a cry of outrage from Senator Howard.

"Now see here!" the senator shouted, coming to his feet. "That is entirely unacceptable! Entirely unacceptable!" His aide laid a hand on the senator's elbow, but Howard shook him off. He planted his fists on the table and leaned forward as if to better see the detective before continuing.

"I am a representative of the highest governmental body in this land, and I won't have my plans delayed by some upstart, badge-toting, backwater flatfoot! You had better rethink your position, my man, if you intend to keep a career in law enforcement. I have friends in high places!"

"What the senator means to say," young Andrews interjected, giving Howard a meaningful glance, and standing to draw attention to himself, "is that he is bearing important documents bound for St. Louis, and it is imperative that they not be delayed."

"Surely the captain has explained that this voyage is to be a special one," Andrews spread his hands imploringly. "We are stopping at only one port, and then only to refuel and reprovision. Now you know the reason."

Senator Howard nodded fiercely as he took his seat again. "We're in something of a hurry," he added with an edge of sarcasm.

Matthews glanced at Captain Manning for confirmation.

"I wasn't aware of the documents," Manning confessed. "But yes, this was to be a quick journey without the usual stops along the way. I guess this explains why."

Matthews rubbed a hand across his face.

"I don't suppose you're missing an assistant, Senator," he said. "Someone who might've been killed to protect you or the documents."

"Sorry," Mr. Andrews spoke up. "There's just the two of us. We thought we'd draw less attention this way."

Howard just glowered at the detective and chewed his cigar.

Ronan spoke up. "I guess it's lucky for you, Matthews, that I happened to book passage on this boat as well. As Captain Manning can tell you, I've helped out with lawmen a time or two in the past. Why not let the captain go ahead and set sail? He can be officially in charge of the investigation aboard ship, and I'll lend him a hand with it. You can continue the investigation here in New Orleans. If either of us learns anything, we can wire the other with the news."

Captain Manning nodded thoughtfully.

Detective Matthews gave Ronan Lynch a long, measuring look, and then he looked sidelong at the fuming senator.

Finally he stuck out his hand.

"Deal," he said.

CHAPTER THREE

"You fool!" the woman hissed. "Why didn't you put more stones on the body? We could have gotten away without anyone being any the wiser until after we reached St. Louis. But now the *Marie Belle's* entire crew is watching for us. We'll have to step carefully from this point on to avoid being exposed."

"I did the best I could," the skinner man responded. "If you remember, you didn't leave me much time. Kill the man, take his clothes and skin, get his riverboat ticket, pitch the body in the river and cover it with rocks, all without being heard or seen by the workmen on the dock right above our heads, and all in time to catch the riverboat before it left. We're lucky we didn't get caught then and there, let alone making it a 'perfect' crime."

"You're always making excuses," she began.

He interrupted. "Well we have a more pressing problem right now, love. The little fool we're saddled with is beginning to suspect that something's wrong! We'll have to do something about that soon."

The skinner woman thought for a moment, in silence. "All right," she said at last. "Here's the plan. I'll wait for you tonight at midnight, down in the cargo hold, near the door to the boiler room. Then we'll simply..."

* * *

The *Marie Belle's* wheel began to turn. It churned the dark river water, splashing rhythmically and raising a sparkling mist into the air. The boat slowly pulled away from the docks and turned her prow northward, gathering speed as she went. The city of New Orleans slowly shrank into the distance behind. As the boat glided up the wide mouth of the Mississippi, mossy elms and willows slid by on either shore, herons stalking among their roots.

Ronan got down to business. First, he interrogated the various crewmembers. Their stories bore out what the captain had said earlier. There was really no way that any one of them could have slipped away to commit the murder, and then slipped back on board, without being seen coming or going by at least one of the others. There had been simply too much work to be accomplished while they were in port, loading and stowing fuel and provisions, cleaning and repairing the boat, and getting the passengers settled in their cabins.

Someone was always headed up or down the gangplank every few minutes, and—the chief engineer and head stewards both confessed—these men all kept a pretty close eye on one another during that time to make sure that everyone was pulling his weight. Let one of the on-duty men start to slack off a little, and the others would be harassing him to get his "lazy behind" moving.

As for the off-duty men, they tended to grab a quick bite to eat and then fall into their bunks for a few hours of exhausted sleep. Of course, even if one of them had stayed awake and slipped off the boat, he would have been spotted on the gangplank by one of the on-duty men. (And undoubtedly he would have been ribbed about not working hard enough during his hours, if he could afford to pass up an opportunity to sleep.)

Now that the boat was underway, the men were all a bit more scattered during their on-duty hours, each one at his particular post, and they had a bit more energy and freedom during their off-duty hours. "They'd certainly have the time to commit a murder now," Ronan thought wryly, "but they couldn't have done it then."

The morning passed. As the sun neared its apex, Ronan began to interview the passengers. He decided to approach them in alphabetical order, as they were recorded on the chief steward's roster. That way none of them could complain that he was singling them out for special interrogation.

If they all believed he didn't yet have a clue, maybe the murderer or murderers would even get sloppy and let something slip. "Trouble was," Ronan mused wryly, "I don't have a damn clue."

SKINNERS

Alphabetically, then, he began with young Mr. Andrews, although he figured that the senator's aide was an unlikely suspect. It came as no surprise that Senator Howard was there as well when he located Mr. Andrews. Ronan found them forward, in the boat's saloon. A cloud of cigar smoke greeted him as he entered.

Howard looked down his nose at the cowboy. "I hope you aren't so thick-headed as to suspect me!" he growled.

Ronan stared hard at him for a long moment, just to show that he wasn't intimidated by the senator's bluster.

"I don't suspect anybody in particular—yet," he growled at last. "Now, why don't you two tell me about your movements this mornin'?"

"Well, Mr. Lynch, the senator and I boarded the boat last night," Andrews explained. "We made special arrangements to take our rooms aboard the boat early, rather than spend another evening in a hotel in town. That way we wouldn't have to rise early in order to be in time for the launch."

"And I'll have you know, Mr. Lynch," the senator added, prodding Ronan in the chest with an extended finger, "that Andrews and I were up most of the night discussing business. My associate never left my side, and I advise you to drop this unorthodox questioning before I have the authorities throw you off of this boat!"

Ronan cocked an eye at the senator, and growled in a low throttle. The man quickly withdrew his finger, took a small step back from the gunslinger, then hurriedly left the room.

His threats were likely an exaggeration (in keeping with the senator's overly dramatic, pompous self-importance), but not by much. Andrews struck Ronan as too dedicated, too professional, too imperturbable, and too open and honest to have committed the murder. Still, that feeling wasn't something that would hold much water in a court of law.

From a purely factual basis, Andrews *could* have done the killing, Ronan supposed. But why skin the man afterward? Andrews just didn't seem the type to go to such extremes. Ronan sighed and crossed Andrews and the senator off the list, at least for now.

*   *   *

Next Ronan went to talk to the newlyweds. He found him in the dining room, having an early lunch. Their backs were to the door by which he entered, so he watched them for a few moments, unobserved. They certainly seemed unlikely suspects as well. Even now, Rita hung on Jack's arm, chatting merrily away at her new husband as he tried to eat. Ronan wondered if Jack ever had a moment alone, even to visit the privy. The thought brought a grin to his lips.

As for Rita, the idea of her having killed and skinned someone seemed positively ludicrous. Ronan remembered her fainting spell at the mere glimpse of the body on the dock. Then a thought occurred to him: Could she have fainted not from horror at the sight, but rather from horror that her handiwork had been discovered? He shook his head. That was ridiculous.

Again, it was possible that Rita had lured the victim under the dock and Jack had attacked him from behind. But Ronan would have bet his soul that this wasn't the case. "Assuming I still have one," he thought. Rita seemed simply too improbable a murderer, and it seemed she always had her eye on Jack, so he could hardly have done the deed either.

Still, it wouldn't hurt to talk with them for a moment. Removing his hat, Ronan crossed to their table and took a seat.

"Good mornin', folks," he said, accepting a cup of coffee from the steward.

Rita paused in her chatter, and Jack glanced up at the new arrival with a forkful of potatoes poised halfway to his mouth. He set it back down on his plate and wiped his mouth.

"So, ma'am, where were you this mornin'?" Ronan asked.

Jack glanced at Rita, and she blushed.

"We came aboard last night," Jack said, speaking slowly and evenly. "Went to our cabin, and tried to get a wink of sleep."

Rita blushed further.

Ronan pretended not to notice. "Didn't I see you down on the dock, Mrs. Baroni?" he asked.

"Yes," Rita answered. "The two of us woke shortly before the boat was to leave, and we decided to go to the dock for a breath of air. Jack went ahead, while I finished dressing. I followed a moment later. That's when I saw the body..." She paled.

Ronan nodded. Their testimony pretty much matched up with what the chief steward had told him. Simms had spotted Jack coming down the gangplank first, hands jammed in his pockets, obviously out for a walk. Rita had followed a few minutes later, looking for Jack.

Jack gave Ronan a cold stare. "I think you've upset her enough," he said.

Ronan stood and put his hat back on. That sort of protective response was just about what he'd expect from a young husband.

"Thanks for the help," he said, and left.

*   *   *

Next on the list was "Tom" Black Eagle. Ronan figured the Indian was most likely in his cabin. So he headed that direction, thinking about what the chief steward had told him of the Indian's arrival.

Simms had said that Black Eagle arrived at the riverboat only minutes before the body was discovered, and he was sweating and out of breath. Simms had the impression that the Indian had run at least part of the way from town to catch the boat.

Further, the ticket he handed over had been stamped and dated just that morning. How Black Eagle had managed to get the agent in town to open his office and sell a ticket so early in the morning was a mystery to the chief steward. The Indian must be a very persuasive man. Still, the ticket was in order, so Simms signed him in and sent him aboard.

Ronan knocked on the door to Black Eagle's cabin. It was one of the smallest ones, near the boat's stern. The paddle wheel made quite a racket this far back.

The Indian opened his door, glanced impassively at the cowboy, and stepped outside to join him on deck, closing the cabin door behind. Ronan caught a quick glimpse of a Navajo rug laid out on the floor inside, walls decorated with beads and feathers, and a thin trail of smoke from a clay pot set on a painted stone. Apparently, the Indian had been praying.

"Sorry if I interrupted somethin'," Ronan said.

Black Eagle waved a hand as if to brush away the apology. He waited, stony-eyed for Ronan to speak further.

Ronan stared for a moment, then took a breath and spoke.

"The chief steward says you were in something of a hurry to get aboard this morning," he said.

Black Eagle merely stared at him.

"Runnin' from somethin', chief?" Ronan asked.

"There is an evil aboard this vessel," Black Eagle replied, "but it is not me. I was not running away, but running after."

"Care to tell me what you mean?" Ronan asked.

"I come seeking a sacred Navajo dagger," Black Eagle said, "a strong magic that allows Navajo shamans to commune with animal spirits, to walk with them. It was stolen from my people. The trail of its thieves has led me here."

He stared intently at Ronan. Suddenly, his eyes grew wide.

"What's the trouble?" Ronan asked.

"There is a darkness upon you," Black Eagle hissed. "You are not what you seem." He made a sign with his hand, presumably to ward off evil.

Ronan took a step backward.

"I will talk to you no longer," the Indian said, grimacing in fear. He opened his cabin door and slipped quickly inside.

Ronan stood staring at the closed door. He could hear Black Eagle chanting again inside, more fervently than before. A chill passed over him, and he headed back toward the bow of the boat. He didn't like the thought that the Indian had maybe caught a glimpse of the thing inside him, and he certainly didn't want Black Eagle peering any deeper into his soul.

Still, Black Eagle's reaction to Ronan's own demon made him suspect that there was no harm in the Indian. Could the victim have been a monster? Ronan wondered. Might Black Eagle have destroyed the man for that reason? If that were the case, why had he boarded the ship once the deed was done? Could it be that there were yet more such monsters aboard?

Ronan decided to leave the Indian alone for now. If the skinner was aboard ship, Black Eagle might turn out to be a valuable ally, though perhaps a not entirely willing one. In any event, there was no use provoking a further confrontation with him, especially considering that Ronan didn't believe he had committed the murder. Destroying a monster was one thing; skinning a man was quite another. And Ronan didn't think Black Eagle would resort to such gruesome tactics.

*   *   *

The cowboy went looking for the next person on his list, Rusty Carmichael. He found the gambler in the aft lounge, nursing a bottle and watching the early afternoon sunlight sparkle on the river. Their conversation was surprisingly revealing. The riverboat gambler—normally the sort of man who remained tight lipped under accusing eyes—was forthright and helpful.

"No, sir," Carmichael said, "I don't have any enemies that I know of. Sure, I make a living off winning money at cards, but I also make a point of being sure there are no hard feelings. I have three rules by which I live." He ticked them off on his fingers.

"First, I don't play against people who can't afford to lose. Riverboats tend to draw a wealthier clientele, and they can usually afford to lose a little money. Of course, that isn't always true, but I've learned to watch people's expressions. You have to, if you're going to be any good at Poker. And I can always tell within a hand or two how losing is setting with a fellow. Some just take it in stride; they're the ones with more money than they know what to do with. Others get a little steamy, but it blows over quickly; they're the ones who just can't stand to lose." He leaned closer to Ronan and added in a whisper, "Like our friend, Senator Howard." He winked. "But if someone's truly desperate for the money, it shows pretty quickly."

"Which brings me to my second rule: Never take a man's last dollar. If I see someone's getting sore, I just excuse myself from the game to go eat or have a smoke. I don't want to ever be the instrument of someone else's financial destruction."

"And that brings me to my third rule: Always give something back." The gambler chuckled. "I will confess, if you'll swear to keep it a secret, that I often purposely lose a little money at the end of a night, to help ease the sting of my winnings. Sometimes I even lose big."

"Always by plan?" Ronan asked.

Carmichael laughed. "Well, the cards don't always smile on me. Everyone has a bad day now and again. Still, I make due overall."

"Well, pardner," Ronan said, "maybe you could put those people skills to work. Let's see if you can help me out a little, and figure out who among them actually might have a reason to see a man killed."

Carmichael grinned. "I never in all my days imagined I'd ever be working as a 'law dog,'" he said. "But sure, I'll keep an eye open and get back to you or the captain if I learn anything."

Ronan left the conversation feeling frankly impressed with the gambler. Carmichael might not be a Sunday-go-to-meeting type, but he clearly had a code to live by, and as codes went, it was one of the better ones Ronan had come across. He wished the gambler luck and set out looking for the next two to question—the MacPhersons.

*   *   *

Not that Ronan seriously suspected them—Ms. Adelia struck him as one of those genuinely puritanical souls to whom the thought of murder would never occur, even if their life actually depended upon it. Nor would she be likely to have any enemies sufficiently pernicious as to warrant killing. People like her might often rub other people the wrong way, but they didn't tend to make serious enemies. Other people were more likely to avoid them than to seek retribution. If the truth be told, even her detractors most likely had a grudging respect for her uprightness. And without enemies after his mother, the silent-but-strong son Randall would certainly have no reason to kill either.

No, the reason Ronan talked with these two was not to establish their innocence. Rather, it was to see if they had any insights into who the killer was. As with Rusty Carmichael, he hoped that these two might turn up a clue or two, perhaps in an overheard conversation, or maybe just from sharp-eyed observation.

He found them sitting in the aft lounge, over cups of tea.

"We don't like to gossip," Ms. MacPherson said sternly, staring at Ronan with flinty eyes. "Though we do understand that it's our Christian duty to help see that this murderer is caught and punished. Still, we certainly wouldn't want to go pointing fingers without some pretty firm evidence. But we will certainly keep our eyes and ears open. If we do discover anything, or remember anything, you will definitely be the first to know."

Randall didn't speak through the entire conversation, deferring to his mother. He nodded when appropriate, and politely stood when Ronan took his leave.

*   *   *

That left only one on the list of passengers, Alice Monroe, the fetching young gal whom Ronan had caught eyeballing him in the dining room that morning. He caught up with her just outside her cabin, and she invited him in for a drink. Somewhat cautiously, he agreed.

"I must admit," she said, lowering her eyes flirtatiously, "That I have been wondering when you would make some time for me on this voyage." She glanced back up at him and smiled.

"Lordy, but this brandy does make a body warm," she added, loosening the bodice of her dress slightly, and fanning herself. "Wouldn't you be more comfortable taking off that jacket?"

"Pardon me, ma'am, but I'm here for a reason," Ronan snorted. "In case you've forgotten, there was a murder, and I'd like to know what you were doing when it happened."

"Mr. Lynch, how would I know anything about such things. I'm an actress, you know. Would you like to see part of my act?" Alice asked coyly. She then proceeded to her wardrobe, and said, "If you could just help me into this costume, I could..."

"That'll be enough, ma'am," Ronan replied.

Her flirtatiousness did convince him of one thing. As far as Ronan could tell, she had no attachments to any of the other men on board the *Marie Belle,* and without an accomplice, she certainly couldn't have committed the crime herself.

Ronan finally took his leave, and said, "I'd be careful when movin' around the boat, ma'am. Try to make sure you stay within earshot of someone. It's quite dangerous, you know."

Miss Monroe laughed and said, "I look forward to the thrill!"

Ronan chuckled and shook his head. "You're quite a woman, Miss Monroe. I wish I coulda met you in another time."

She gave him a playful smile. "I'm just joshing, Mr. Lynch. But you know," she moved closer, and placed a dainty hand on his chest, "I'd be a lot safer if you were to chaperone me during the rest of the trip." She made to lay her head against him.

"Excuse me, ma'am" he said, "but I've gotta figure out what's goin' on around here, or a lot more folks may wind up with their throats opened."

She made a pout. "Oh, very well," she said. "I'll be good."

Ronan tilted his head in a slight bow, and left, laughing to himself as the door closed behind him. "It's a damn shame."

Chapter Four

Ronan strode the deck alone, grumbling in frustration. It was well past midnight, but he couldn't sleep. He had spent the entire day talking with passengers and crew, but he was no closer to an answer than before.

Maybe Detective Matthews was having a better time of things back in New Orleans. Maybe the killer was there and just happened to leave his victim's body beneath the dock where the *Marie Belle* was tied. Maybe this had nothing to do with the *Marie Belle* at all.

"Maybe," Ronan thought to himself, "but I doubt it!" He just knew that the *Marie Belle* had everything to do with the murder, that the bastard was on board, right now. He had learned to trust his guts in such things. He might not have the detective's training and skills in ferreting out clues, but he had dealt with plenty of villains before, and he knew that sooner or later they always made a mistake—they always gave themselves away.

Having questioned and discounted everyone, Ronan was left with no one to suspect. It was maddening. Hardly more than a dozen people aboard, and apparently none of them could have committed the murder. Unless there was someone else hiding out on the *Marie Belle*. But the boat simply wasn't big enough to hide someone for long.

Still, to be on the safe side, Ronan had asked the chief steward to open all the empty cabins for him, and to take him on a tour of the boat. Not surprisingly, they found nothing.

Ronan wandered along, from one deck to another, and the longer he wandered the madder he got. He climbed to the crew deck, hoping maybe that the view from that height would inspire in him an insight into his problem. Ronan wasn't used to this kind of action. He preferred to pull his pistol and solve a situation as quickly as possible.

Still no answers, and still more frustation. He wanted to pull his iron and fire into the air. "Damn this whole mess," he muttered. "What the Hell am I doing here? This ain't my kinda fight!"

Reversing his steps, Ronan descended to the main deck, and then decided to prowl the cargo hold. Maybe something there would make a connection. It was dim down in the hold, lit only by occasional lanterns, all turned low. He found the darkness somehow comforting, as if here he could hide from the frustration for a few moments.

He wandered past the boiler room. Near the door, his boot heel slipped on a wet spot, freshly mopped. For a second, the fact didn't really register—he just took it in stride. Then he went back to look again. Why was this one spot freshly mopped, when the rest of the area was dry? Lifting a lantern from its hook, he bent down to examine the floor. Nothing.

Then he noticed a small stain on the lower edge of the boiler room door. A dark, red stain. A smear of blood. He set the lantern on the floor and drew his pistol. Cautiously, he turned the door handle and pulled. It was silent inside the boiler room, but for the crackle of flames.

Ronan risked a glance around the door. The boiler room was empty. That was odd; there should be an engineer here stoking coal to keep the paddle wheels turning. Inside, the door to the firebox stood open. That was even odder. It spilled heat wastefully into the boiler room itself. And Ronan thought he smelled the faint scent of roasted flesh.

He entered the room and bent to look in the firebox. Heat waves danced upon the heap of glowing coals inside. But it seemed that there was something more. He used a coal scoop to stir the coals, kicking up the fire. In the flare of light, he recognized the distinctive shapes of bones—lots of them—and flames dancing within the eye sockets of two scorched human skulls.

CHAPTER FIVE

Breakfast found Captain Manning and Ronan addressing the assembly of passengers once again. All except one, that is. Alice Monroe was nowhere to be found aboard the *Marie Belle*. Or rather, it would seem that she had been found, by Ronan, in the firebox last night. The crew had already been spoken to, again all except one missing engineer whose body had apparently joined Miss Monroe's in the fire.

"Considering this latest discovery," Captain Manning was saying to all assembled, "Mister Lynch and I both agree that we simply *must* call a halt to the voyage in Memphis this evening, where we can call on the assistance of their constabulary."

Senator Howard started to object, but the captain simply spoke louder, drowning out whatever the senator might have planned to say. Howard sat back down, gape-mouthed, face flushed crimson with anger or embarrassment. For a moment, it seemed he might actually have a stroke. Ronan winced inwardly, fearful for what effect this might have on the captain's career in the long run. But Manning seemed certain of himself.

"As captain of this boat," he continued, "my first responsibility is to your safety. We have already lost three people, one under the dock in New Orleans, and two more last night. I simply cannot and will not risk any more deaths. If any of you have complaints about my decision," he glanced meaningfully at the senator, "you can lodge a protest with the authorities once we reach Memphis. Until that time, I'm afraid that my decision stands firm. Thank you."

Manning took his leave, and Ronan stepped forward to speak.

"I strongly suggest," he said, "that y'all return to your cabins and remain locked in until we reach Memphis. Or if you prefer, some of you might gather here in the dining room or forward in the smokin' salon. But—if you value your life—don't wander the ship alone."

The Baronis left, as did Mrs. MacPherson and her son, apparently headed for their cabins.

The senator rose, gesturing for his aide to follow. He paused in passing Ronan.

"We will be in the saloon, having a smoke," he said. "And if I were you, I would do my best to convince the captain to change his mind about halting the voyage at Memphis. It is a decision he is liable to regret, and soon."

Ronan balled his fists and the crackling of his knuckles penetrated the air, and he took a few steps towards the senator. But Ronan second guessed whooping the little man, and he pulled up before he made a mistake he probably wouldn't regret.

Milton and Andrews left in a hurry. Black Eagle followed immediately after them, staring hard at Ronan as he passed by him and out of the room.

That left only Carmichael. He grinned at the cowboy.

"Well, I guess I'll go join the senator and young Mr. Andrews," he said. "Maybe get them interested in a poker game to help pass the time." He clapped Ronan on the shoulder on the way out.

Ronan took a last look around the empty room, then headed for the main deck to think some more.

CHAPTER SIX

"Damn that Ronan Lynch!" the man said. "We should just kill him and have done with it."

"Easier said than done," the woman cautioned. "But I agree that he is a thorn in our sides. He would have to come along last night just as we were cleaning up in the boiler room. Just another few minutes, and no one would have been the wiser."

"We certainly don't want to undergo a thorough investigation at Memphis," he said.

"That's why I say we should deal with the captain," she answered. "We can circumvent Mister Lynch entirely."

"I see your point," he responded. "Yes. Let's do deal with the captain next, by all means. When next he goes to his cabin, you lure him out, and I'll take care of him."

"That's my good baby," she cooed.

*   *   *

The *Marie Belle* paddled furiously against the Mississippi's current. Another couple of days would have seen it reach St. Louis. Under the current plan, however, a few more hours would find it docked indefinitely at Memphis. Once cleared by the authorities there (a matter of a couple of days, most likely), most of the passengers could either book passage on another riverboat or ride the rails on to St. Louis.

The delay would be an inconvenience for them. "Not near as much of one as bein' killed," Ronan thought. He only hoped that in sifting through the passengers the authorities would identify the killer.

The sun was just dropping below the churning paddle wheel, its reddening light tinting the foam pink, like blood from a lung-shot man, when Ronan noted Captain Manning passing by in a hurry.

"How much longer to Memphis?" Ronan asked.

"Oh, I don't know," Manning replied. "Maybe an hour? Maybe two? Not long now, I would say. I should tell you, however, that I've reconsidered about halting the voyage there."

"What the Hell...?" Ronan responded, incredulously. "That's not what you agreed to!"

Manning raised an admonishing hand. "Now, now," he said. "It's my decision to make, and I've decided that it's best if we press on."

"Why is that, pardner?" Ronan asked.

The captain frowned. "Well," he began, "It's just that, you see, I was thinking..." He paused.

Ronan jumped in. "You understand we have a monster somewhere on board, and yet you want to continue on and give whoever it is even more time to kill?"

Manning glared at the cowboy. "Yes, I know there's a killer on board," he said. "And as a matter of fact, that's exactly why I don't want to stop longer than necessary for fuel and supplies. I don't want it escaping to wreak havoc in the city. Better if we deal with it ourselves, here aboard ship."

Ronan glared back. "Somethin' isn't right here," he said. "You ain't telling me everything, old friend."

"I'm the captain," Manning replied archly. "I don't have to tell you everything."

Ronan stared at him in confusion. "Are you the same Darius Manning I spoke with this mornin'?" he asked. "Because the Darius Manning I see now talks like a damn fool."

The captain's eyes grew wide. Manning turned and walked briskly away.

"Hold it!," Ronan shouted. "I'm not finished with you."

Manning broke into a run.

"What the Hell are you doing" Ronan cried. He trotted after the man.

The captain cast a panicked glance back over his shoulder. He dashed down a flight of stairs to the main deck, and headed for the bow. He moved with the energy of a man less than half his age.

Ronan pursued. In passing, he noted the faces of passengers in the windows of their cabins. They were watching the race with great interest.

"Stop, Darius!" Ronan shouted, drawing his pistol. Had the killer have been the captain all along? He knew Darius, and had known him for some time. It was hard to believe that he could be a murderer, and such a monstrous one at that. And still, the captain fled.

Manning glanced back, then ran for the rail. He dove over it and split the water cleanly, disappearing from view in the dark waters for a moment.

Ronan reached the rail. Behind him sounded the footsteps of other passengers and crew, coming to discover what was happening.

The captain's head broke the surface of the river. Manning dog paddled in a circle for a moment, turning to face the nearest shore. Then his eyes suddenly grew wide, and he began thrashing in a panic.

As those on the riverboat watched, a strange transformation came over the swimmer. First, the skin on his face and hands began to sag and stretch, filling with river water. His features pulled askew on his skull, one set of eyelids sliding down onto his cheekbone, his lower lip pulling loose from his chin.

He screamed. Skin was sliding up out of the collar of his shirt, now, and spreading in flabby layers upon the surface of the river. His thrashing hands were revealed as nothing but muscle and bone. His scalp had slid forward to cover his eyes.

His screams were growing frantic. Desperately, he tried to swim back to the boat, but the ever-loosening skin hindered him, obscuring his sight and tangling his limbs.

His struggles grew weaker. Soon, all that remained floating on the surface of the dark river was his pale, empty skin.

An awful silence hovered over the group clustered at the rail. They glanced at one another in horrible wonderment. Mrs. McPherson began trembling violently. Her eyes rolled up in her head, and she collapsed to the deck. Randall tried to catch her just a moment too late. She lay motionless, her face gray. Carmichael bent to check her pulse. He looked back up at Randall, who stood there in shock.

"She's dead," the gambler said.

Randall put his face into his hands and wept, his big, bony frame shaking with heartbroken sobs.

CHAPTER SEVEN

Ronan stalked the decks in a fury. He had ordered the other passengers back to their cabins, then went looking for the pilot, McCombs.

"You're the captain, now," Ronan said when he found him. "But I'm takin' charge, and if you don't like it, tell me now." He meaningfully dropped a hand onto the handle of his gun.

"That's fine," the new captain answered, nodding rapidly. "You're in charge. What are your orders?"

"Just get us to Memphis," Ronan said. "And don't let anyone convince you otherwise."

"Yes, sir," McCombs responded. "I mean 'no, sir.' I mean..."

"I know what you mean, McCombs," Ronan told him. "Now get to it!"

With the new captain installed in the wheelhouse, Ronan began tramping about the decks, mind racing, trying to make sense of the horror he and the others had seen. Black Eagle had mentioned something about a ritual dagger and communing with animals. Maybe he meant wearing animal skins. Was this monster able to take that practice a step further, to wear people's skins?

Ronan thought back to Manning's supposition on the first day that someone had lured the first victim below the dock, where an accomplice had attacked. If that was truly the case, it meant that there was likely another skinner on board right now. But who?

A figure beckoned to him from an open doorway. It was Alice Monroe!

"Shhh," she whispered, imploring him with her eyes. She glanced about fearfully. "Please," she said. "You have to help me! I know who they are. I overheard them talking, which is why I've been hiding. If they find me, they'll kill me for sure!"

Ronan gazed, slack-jawed, at her.

"This way," she said. "I'll show you where they are." She slipped back into the darkness.

Ronan followed. As he stepped through the doorway, he caught a furtive motion to the right side.

He turned, reaching for his revolver.

Alice cracked him in the head with a crowbar.

He went down, dazed.

She hit him again, and the world went black.

CHAPTER EIGHT

Ronan woke to awful pain. His every nerve seemed doused in liquid flame. His eyes were wide open, and when he tried to blink, he couldn't. The muscles just wouldn't respond.

Moaning, he levered himself to his knees. His raw flesh stuck to the wooden slats of the floor as he tried to rise, tearing loose in searing agony when he pulled harder. He lurched to his feet in the dark cabin, felt for his gunbelt.

There was none. He was naked. No, worse than naked. He could feel the bones of his hips, the very bones! He lifted a hand to his face, and felt bony fingertips tap against lipless teeth.

"The bitch skinned me!" he half howled, half slurred. With his lips missing, he couldn't form the words just right.

Then cold anger swept over him. He would make her pay. Wherever she was, he'd find her and make her pay dearly for this violation. And for all the other victims she and her accomplice had murdered. How or why they had done it didn't matter to him at all, only that she be stopped, and that she suffer something of the agony he now felt.

Ronan laughed, low and gurgling. Wouldn't she be surprised he wasn't dead. Sometimes the demon inside of him wasn't so bad after all. Especially when it kept him kicking.

Blindly, Ronan felt his way to the door, threw it open. Lamplight from the deck outside lit the room, revealing the walking horror that he had become. Arms, torso, and legs, all revealed naked muscle over glistening bone. He knew his face must be a grinning skull thinly covered by patches of meat.

Ronan spotted a gunbelt with a single pistol hanging from a hook on the inside of the door. It must have belonged to the first skinner, the male. He buckled the gunbelt around his hips, ignoring the fresh pain of its contact with his flesh, and strode forth, a flame-eyed specter from some madman's Hell, to find the skinner woman.

On the way to the stairs, he saw smoke coming from beneath the door to Black Eagle's cabin. From inside, he could hear the Indian chanting a Navajo prayer, his voice thick with fear.

Ronan pounded on the door, leaving bloody prints where his fist impacted with the door. "Black Eagle!" he shouted. "What's going on in there?" Without lips to help frame the words, his voice came out slurred, though understandable.

Black Eagle continued to chant his prayer.

"Black Eagle!" Ronan shouted, pounding again.

The chanting stopped. Black Eagle coughed. Smoke was curling thicker from the lower edge of the door.

"Go away!" Black Eagle cried. "I will not open the door. I have set fire to the boat, so that the skinner will be trapped and perish. If you wish to live, then leap from the deck and swim. The skinner cannot swim." He started to pray again, his voice rising to a scream as the door began to blister and smoke billowed from beneath it.

"Damn fool!" Ronan shouted, driven back by the growing heat. His eyeballs teared, but he could not blink away the smoke or the moisture.

More quickly now, he stalked the length of the deck and climbed the stairs to the next one up. By the time he reached the top, the deck below was like a furnace. Hellish flames leapt into the air all along the boat's port side. The passengers staggered about in a panic, while crewmen struggled to dowse the fire with buckets of sand.

SKINNERS

Then one of the engineers spotted Ronan, and cried out in abject terror. Passengers and crew alike fled from the sight of him. They ran to the opposite rail and leapt overboard to escape this new horror. Ronan wished them luck in reaching the shore.

He knew that the skinner woman must still be on board, however. Maybe he could spot her from the pilothouse. He shambled off in that direction.

As he climbed the stairway to the crew deck, Ronan recognized Senator Howard ahead, near the pilothouse, glancing about in confusion. There was no one else on the deck; McCombs must have left the pilothouse to help fight the fire below, then fled with everyone else when Ronan appeared.

The senator carried a carpetbag in his left hand. Ronan thought that perhaps it contained the precious documents he was protecting. Spotting Ronan, Howard gave a sudden start. His eyes grew wide.

"You!" the fat man cried, then he collected himself and dashed up the stairs and into the pilothouse, and locked the door at the top of the stairs. He dropped the carpetbag on the floor, below the level of the windows, then bent to open it. He came back up with a flint dagger in one hand, and a large bundle of feathers in the other, apparently the pelt of an eagle or other great bird of prey.

"Stop!," Ronan yelled, then he pursued him up to the pilothouse. He looked through the window in the door, and saw the senator standing over his bag.

The senator began to remove his clothes, tearing them open, even using the knife to rip them free. The swelling firelight from the decks below revealed a blubbery belly and flabby arms.

He dropped the last of his clothing and tore open the skin on his chest and stomach, peeling it wide! He slipped the skin off his head and arms, and sloughed it off like an old suit. Ronan saw now that the rolls of fat underneath were bound to the senator's torso by bloody strips of linen. Then suddenly, he realized, this was not the senator. This was the skinner woman!

She used the flint knife to sever the bloody strips, and the slabs of fat she had harvested from the senator's body, to pad out his pelt, fell free. She stood there for a moment, horribly skinless herself. Then with her right elbow, she drew back and gave the center forward window a hefty strike. It held. She drew back again, revealing the bloody splotch from the first blow, and struck the window a second time, shattering it. Then she tossed the eagle pelt across her shoulders, and before Ronan's eyes, began to transform. By the time Ronan forced the door open, she had shifted shapes into that of a great bird of prey. As an eagle, she leapt through the shattered window and into the sky, the flint knife clutched in one taloned foot.

Pumping her wings furiously, she began to climb.

PAGE 26

Grimly, Ronan drew his borrowed pistol.

The eagle spiraled upward, then turned toward the river's east bank.

Ronan took aim, and fired.

His shot missed, and the eagle dove to gain speed, pulling up just short of the water.

The riverboat lurched over onto its wounded side and rapidly began to sink.

Ronan rode the movement and fired again.

The eagle's head and wings jerked up spastically, and it crashed into the water. Almost immediately, the skin began to come loose, and a figure half eagle and half human splashed about frantically, screaming in a woman's voice. As Ronan watched, the thrashing grew steadily weaker. The scream faded to a gurgle, then died out entirely. The Mississippi flowed smoothly over the spot where the skinner had crashed down.

Ronan stared out across the river's surface, his grinning skull visage incapable of any other expression.

As the flames danced about his shins, a thought suddenly struck him. The carpet bag! She must have carried her stolen skins in it! If his was there, then maybe, just maybe...!

The boat was sinking fast. The main deck was submerged already, and water poured through the ship's shattered windows. As its roof sank beneath the river's surface, Ronan dove after it. The waters closed over his head, and the *Marie Belle* rolled over and sank beneath the pitch black river.

EPILOGUE

A coyote trotted along the western bank of the river. It smelled meat, bloody, slightly rank, somewhere nearby. It whined and yipped in hunger, hoping to find the carcass before something larger did.

Its nose led it to a sandbank at a bend in the river. A crescent moon hung low in the sky, tangled among the skeletal branches of a dead oak. The glowing curve looked for all the world like the disembodied smile of a Cheshire cat, grinning down upon the scene.

Under its light, the coyote spotted a figure cast up on the sandbar. By the scent, it was human, dead for some time. The coyote trotted nearer, whining its nervousness, sniffing the air, alert for trouble. It snuffled the meat—raw meat, skinless, just muscle and bone.

The meat groaned, and the coyote danced back, growling in frustration and fear. The meat staggered to its feet, clutching a soggy suit of skin in its hand.

"Shoo!" it shouted, lunging forward.

The coyote fled, yelping, to seek easier prey.

SKINNERS

THE ADVENTURE

The world of *Deadlands* is one of mystery and fear. These two concepts certainly go hand in hand, for the unknown is the most fearful thing of all.

This adventure leads the posse through a mysterious and terrifying series of events, to eventual recognition of a unique and unexpected horror.

Chances are, the heroes won't realize what's really happening until late in the course of events. That isn't to say that they have no choices in the adventure, however. Their actions certainly affect the lives of their fellow passengers aboard the riverboat on which the events take place, and eventually determine whether the villains get away with their crimes, and their stolen artifact.

Keep in mind, though, that the purpose of this adventure is not really for the players to figure out the mystery. Instead, it is primarily that they "enjoy the ride." Certainly, by adventure's end, they should have discovered the facts necessary to build a complete picture of the evil they have faced and, hopefully, defeated.

By the way, this adventure can serve as a great starting point for a campaign, because the heroes don't even have to know one another at the beginning. They just all need some reason to be traveling by riverboat from New Orleans to St. Louis. The events of the story will introduce them all to one another, and the mystery will give them a reason to become a posse.

THE STORY SO FAR

Among Native American tribes, there have long been legends of "shapechangers" and "skinwalkers." These people were able to take the form of an animal by wearing its magically treated pelt. According to the tales, living for a while in an animal's skin gives a person a new perspective on the world, a deep and abiding reverence for the sanctity and interconnectedness of all living things, and a new appreciation for nature.

But like a disease, the Reckoners corrupt all they touch. Recently, two evil hucksters have stolen a sacred dagger the Navajo Indians once used to prepare pelts for skinwalking, and have turned it to a sinister new use.

Twisting the power that resides in this ancient artifact, they have learned to skin not only animals, but even other humans, and to wear those human skins to pass themselves off as their victims. This has required a great sacrifice on their part, however. In order to bond to these human skins, the "skinners" first had to prepare their own bodies by flaying each other alive!

Now, these mad villains hope to escape Back East with the sacred dagger and their packet of pelts. They are being pursued by Black Eagle, an Navajo shaman, who is aware of their evil ways.

They've brutally murdered a couple of riverboat passengers and stolen their tickets (and skins). It's their plan to ride the riverboat traveling up the Mississippi to St. Louis, then cross the border into the USA and catch a train for New York.

The skinners' first victim was a lovely young actress named Alice Monroe. She was murdered by the skinners the night before the boat leaves New Orleans.

The morning before the voyage begins, they murder Jack Baroni. He and his wife Rita are newlyweds.

The skinner woman, Janice, is portraying Alice. Her partner, Emerson, is wearing Jack's skin. Will the posse uncover their scheme and put a halt to it? Or will these hideous skinners escape to prey upon the gentrified citizens of the East?

THE SKINNERS

These two mad hucksters, Emerson Walker and Janice Humphries, have grand plans for themselves as eventual secret masters over New York. Sadly, their vision is much grander than their abilities—or their sanity.

Slightly off kilter to begin with, they drove themselves further over the edge through the pain of skinning each other in order to become skin-trading creatures. Still, they are good enough at pretending to be their victims that most people are fooled. Now they just need to get back to the East from the West, and then start their mad scheme.

Janice is the brains of the pair; she retains her self control even when things begin to get dodgy. Emerson contributes mainly muscle, and he fidgets a bit when nervous.

JANICE HUMPHRIES

Janice Humphries is an evil woman who has always felt that life owed her more than she has received. She is highly intelligent, but twisted. She uses her know-how and sick views on life to bend the rules in order to get ahead.

Her first step to get ahead was to learn the ways of the huckster. She was convinced that magic was a means to her fortune and glory.

She met and recruited her partner, Emerson Walker, while out West. Janice is the brains behind their operation, and she continually orders her companion around.

PROFILE

Corporeal: D:4d8, N:4d10, Q:2d12, S:3d8, V:4d8
Climbin' 5d10, dodge 3d12, fightin': brawlin' 2d12, filchin' 4d10, lockpickin' 2d12, shootin': pistol 3d10, sneak 4d12
Mental: C:4d10, K:3d8, M:3d10, Sm:5d10, Sp:3d10
Bluff 2d12, disguise 4d12, persuasion 3d12, scroungin' 1d12, streetwise 2d12
Edges: Keen 3, nerves of steel 1, purty 1, tough as nails 1
Hindrances: Bloodthirsty -2, greedy -2, loco (sociopathic) -3, mean as a rattler -2
Pace: 10
Wind: 20

SKINNERS

Special Abilities:

Invulnerability: The skins Janice wears make her invulnerable to damage. Each location of the skin can take 5 wound levels before it is destroyed, and then Janice may be harmed normally in those locations.

Skinning: When using the dagger and her knowledge of its powers, this gives Janice the ability to shift her own shape into that of an animal that she skins. She becomes the animal until she sheds its skin. Janice can also don skins taken from other people. She gains no knowledge from the victim. Janice does, however, have an uncanny knack for mimicry, and this is reflected above in her high *disguise* rating.

Terror: 9 (but only when she is without a skin).

Vulnerability: The skinners, lacking true body fat, cannot swim. Whenever a skinner falls into water that is more than head high, she will sink and drown.

Gear: Remington 2-shot pistol, a carpetbag full of skins, and the magical Navajo skinning knife: In her hands, it can harvest the skins of other people for her to wear.

Description: Janice, without a skin, is a horribly gruesome sight. She is simply a bloody human figure, with all musculature and bones exposed, and she oozes blood from her entire body. She must wear a skin or risk losing blood continually. When she is wearing someone else's skin, she literally becomes that person. Her voice and eye color match the victims, but her mannerisms may be slightly different. She must study her victims' actions if she wants to mimic them closely. She also carries her own skin, and the pelt of an eagle, in her bag.

EMERSON WALKER

Emerson is the somewhat nervous, unobtrusive partner of Janice Humphries. He follows her orders exclusively.

PROFILE

Corporeal: D:3d10, N:3d12, Q:3d12, S:4d10, V:4d10

Dodge 4d12, fightin': brawlin' 4d12, shootin': revolver 4d10, throwin' 4d10

Mental: C:2d6, K:3d4, M:3d6, Sm:1d8, Sp:3d10

Bluff 4d8, disguise 3d10 (unrelated to his skinner abilities), survival 3d8

Edges: Kemosabe (Navajo ways) 2, knack (can sense magic to 50 feet) 5

Hindrances: Bloodthirsty –2, clueless –3, loco (sociopathic) –2, loyal (to Janice Humphries) –3

Pace: 12

Wind: 20

Special Abilities:

 Skinning: Like his partner, Emerson can wear the skins of animals and of other people.

 Invulnerability: same as Janice, described above.

 Terror: 9 (without a skin).

 Vulnerability: See Janice's description above.

Gear: .44 Army pistol

Description: Like Janice, Emerson is a horrid creature without his skin. He is wearing Jack Baroni's skin at the start of the adventure.

"TOM" BLACK EAGLE

Black Eagle is typically grimly serious, which isn't surprising considering his mission on the ship. He belongs to the tribe from which the skinners stole the sacred dagger, and he has been tracking them to recover it and punish them for their crimes against his tribe.

His search has led him to the river city of New Orleans. Black Eagle is a little on the edge, but he is a fair man with an important mission on his hands. It's obvious that the city makes him nervous.

Black Eagle found Alice Monroe's skinless remains shortly after she was killed, though of course he has no idea of what her name is or what she would look like with her skin on. In the warehouse where her carcass was left, he found a crumpled flybill advertising the *Marie Belle,* and so he's come to the riverboat in hopes of finding her killers.

PROFILE

Corporeal: D:2d10, N:3d8, S:2d10, Q:3d8, V:4d10

Bow 3d10, shootin': rifle 4d10, climbin' 3d10, sneak 3d10

Mental: C:3d10, K:2d8, M:5d6, Sm:3d10, Sp:2d12

Animal handlin' 4d8, faith 3d12, language: English 3d8, language: Navajo, search 4d10, survival 2d12, tale tellin' 3d8, trackin' 4d12

Edges: Nerves o' steel 1, rank: Navajo 2, sand 4
Hindrances: Big britches -3, grim servant o' death -5
Pace: 8
Wind: 22
Gear: Bowie knife, medicine bag with healing herbs.
Description: A Navajo Indian in his early forties, "Tom" Black Eagle is just a little under what is considered average height, but he possesses a powerfully muscular build. He doesn't carry much with him, preferring to live the simple life, and he dresses in a brown serge suit topped off with a derby.

THE DAGGER

A 16-inch weapon of charcoal-gray flint, this dagger is inscribed all over with animal pictograms. Its handle is wrapped with bear skin.

The dagger was originally made for ritually preparing animal skins for use as shape-changing totems. By donning the pelt of an animal slain and skinned with this dagger, a Navajo shaman could change into that beast, in order to live as that creature within the world of Nature.

In the hands of the "skinners" of this adventure, the dagger has taken on a much more sinister function. The villains are using it to skin humans in order to impersonate them.

Power: When used to skin an animal, the dagger imbues the pelt with magical properties. The pelt, though removed, retains its link to nature, and the wielder can use it to take on the form of the animal from which it was taken, including its voice and eye color. The effect lasts for as long as the pelt is worn.

Taint: When used for "unnatural" purposes, such as skinning humans, the dagger can affect the user in a negative way. The user becomes *bloodthirsty, mean as a rattler,* suffers from *night terrors,* and is hunted by the Navajo.

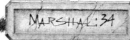

THE SETUP

The driving mystery of this adventure is that the villains are never who they seem to be; they are always disguised in someone else's skin. Not knowing this, the posse can hardly be expected to keep track of who is who as the skinners jump from one identity to another. But it is imperative that the Marshal knows who they are disguised as, what their goals are in those different disguises, and how the other extras in the adventure react. When you're ready to begin, read this to your posse:

In the heat of this late summer, you have each decided to make a trip up the Mississippi River, either for business or pleasure. Starting in New Orleans, you board a riverboat bound for St. Louis.

The riverboat trip is scheduled to take roughly six days, with only one stop, at Memphis, late on the third day, to take on fresh supplies of food and drink. No other dockings are scheduled, because you are sharing the trip with one of the boats owners, the wealthy widower Ms.

McPherson, and a CSA senator from Alabama who wants to enjoy the luxury of a riverboat journey, but doesn't want to stop at every pier on the way.

The first morning of your trip, you rise before the sun and leave your New Orleans hotel, headed for the docks. The sky is still dark as, dressed in light, summer traveling clothes and carrying a week's worth of luggage, you climb the gangway to the deck of the Marie Belle, *as pretty a stern-wheeled boat as ever there was. She seems somehow otherworldly in the dim light of her gas lanterns and the torches on the dock.*

As you step on deck, the ship's steward welcomes you aboard, then checks your ticket and points you toward your cabin. He informs you that a light breakfast of sweet rolls and coffee will be served in two hours in the dining room, and the boat will shove off half an hour later. You have time to stow your luggage and look around the ship a little before breakfast.

CHAPTER ONE: WELCOME ABOARD

The heroes should take the opportunity to look around the ship, meet the crew, and acquaint themselves with the other passengers as they arrive.

THE CREW

The *Marie Belle* has a small crew, composed of the Captain, pilot, the crew (known as the ship's hands), and the stewards who are responsible for taking care of the passengers.

CAPTAIN DARIUS MANNING

Tall and thin, with huge hands, a weathered face, and thick white hair, Manning is an experienced riverboat captain. He is nearly 50 years old, and he has spent 35 of them aboard ship. He loves piloting along the river, in fair weather or foul, and can be trusted to see the boat safely through just about any circumstance of wind or water. He frequently gets assignments for voyages carrying important persons of government or business, such as the voyage in this adventure.

BART MCCOMBS

McCombs, the pilot of the *Marie Belle*, is basically a younger version of Captain Manning. At twenty-nine years old, of course, he has much less experience with the river than does Manning, but he has the same air of confidence. He is shorter and stockier than the captain, but moves with the grace of a natural athlete.

SHIP'S HANDS

There are eight sailing crewmen aboard ship, working four crewmen to each six-hour shift. Each shift is composed of two bosuns and two engineers.

None are remarkable in any way, and they have been taught to stay out from under the passengers' feet, so there is no need to detail them. They won't cause any trouble among the posse, but if questioned repeatedly during the investigation, they may become agitated (as anyone would when questioned about a gruesome murder).

If it becomes necessary to speak of them to the players, simply characterize one as "the old hand," another as "the teen-aged crewman," and so on. They are all typical sailing men, and their role in the adventure is small, but feel free to use them for interesting plot twists at any time.

THE STEWARDS

In addition to the eight sailors, there are three stewards working aboard the ship (see below). Together, they are responsible for preparing meals, serving the passengers, and making sure everyone is comfortable.

ABLE SIMMS

Simms, the Chief Steward, is a warm, likeable fellow with an easygoing personality. He always has a knack for noting what people need next, and he goes out of his way to make sure they get it.

A man in his mid thirties, he is of medium height and weight, with wavy brown hair, brown eyes, and a ready smile. Simms makes you feel comfortable just by being around him.

Like Captain Manning, Simms is frequently assigned to voyages with important personages in attendance. This trip has some notable folks as passengers, and Able is fully aware of its importance.

ASSISTANT STEWARDS

Both in their early twenties, these two men are basically window dressing. To keep them separate, describe one as short and portly, the other as unusually thin and suffering from early baldness.

Captain Manning

Bart McCombs

Able Simms

Senator Howard

Jefferson Andrews

Jack Baroni

Rita Baroni

Adelia McPherson

Randall McPherson

Rusty Carmichael

Alice Monroe

Black Eagle

Detective Matthews

THE PASSENGERS

MILTON HOWARD

A fat, blustery, self-important little man, Senator Howard likes cigars, whiskey, and unquestioning obedience. He has attained his station in life primarily through the judicious use of a family fortune. He does take his duty seriously, seeing himself as having a destiny to make life better for the citizenry.

JEFFERSON ANDREWS

Andrews is a young red headed, freckled law student with dreams of someday becoming president. He is considerably more intelligent than the senator he works for, but lacks both the older man's experience and political savvy.

JACK AND RITA BARONI

When the adventure begins, Jack Baroni has already been killed by the skinners, who need his passage on the riverboat. In appearance, he is of average height, with the slimness of youth, deep blue eyes and curly black hair.

Jack's wife, Rita, has noticed that he is acting strangely, but she thinks that his emotional distance, and his attention to Alice Monroe, are ways of getting even with her for an argument they had on the morning before the trip began.

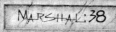

Rita is slightly shorter than average, just a bit on the plump side, with curly blond hair and gray eyes. In personality, she is a simple, guileless person who shows her emotions and naively assumes that everyone around her tries their best to be good. Jack and Rita arrived and slept on the boat last night.

ADELIA MCPHERSON

Mrs. McPherson is a cranky woman in her early seventies who has outlived three husbands, accumulating a fortune in the process. She is a part owner of the *Marie Belle*. A tall, bony woman, she is wrinkled, age-spotted, and balding—but she dresses well.

RANDALL MCPHERSON

It isn't easy to be the offspring of a wealthy parent. Some such children establish themselves by rebelling; others try not to rock the boat, and are treated like children their whole life. Randall falls into the latter category.

A tall, bony man in his late forties, Randall is a compassionate, tender soul, and his mother tramples over him as a result. But his strength is his forgiveness. Randall truly understands his mother, and doesn't care that she treats him with little respect. He has enough self-respect for the both of them.

"RUSTY" CARMICHAEL

"Rusty" used to be a heart-breakingly handsome man, tall, clear eyed, dark haired, and leanly muscular, with a ready wit. Too much boozing has taken the edge off his attractiveness, giving him watery eyes and a slight belly. But he still knows how to dress well, and he is a whiz at poker. He makes his living from gambling and courting middle-aged women.

ALICE MONROE

This unfortunate young woman fell prey to the skinners days ago, merely because she mentioned having had a riverboat ticket and she roughly matched Janice Humphries size and build, Alice has a ripe figure, a pretty face, and brown eyes and hair.

To those aboard the riverboat, Alice seems to have dramatic shifts in personality, and she is unpredictable.

BRIAN MATTHEWS

Detective Matthews (who comes onboard later to conduct his investigation) is a lean, blond man in his early forties. When speaking officially, he is the very picture of calmness but firmness. Privately, however, he can be a bit acerbic, rolling his eyes and sighing as he mutters a sarcastic comment about the sad state of humanity.

THE SHIP

Fear Level 2

The *Marie Belle* is a typical steam-powered, stern-wheeled riverboat, roughly 200 feet long and 40 feet wide, with two railed decks devoted to passengers, a cargo hold below, a crew deck above them for the steering house and crews' quarters, and a pilot house atop it all.

The *Marie Belle* is an elegant means of traveling along the Mississippi. Its two passenger decks allow for a lavish central dining room with a high ceiling and a second-floor balcony. Mahogany paneling abounds, with many large windows to allow daylight into the various public rooms. Gas lamps keep the boat lit even at night.

On this voyage in particular, the cuisine is magnificent (in deference to the presence of both the outspoken Senator Howard and the wealthy Mrs. McPherson—who needless to say also owns the boat), and the bar is well stocked with wines, high quality ales, and fancy liqueurs from all over the world.

The crew is on their best behavior. Able Simms, the Chief Steward, is even more delightful than normal and assists the guests in any way possible, especially the Senator or Mrs. McPherson.

PILOTHOUSE DECK

Description: This topmost deck of the *Marie Belle* measures roughly 15 feet wide by 35 feet long. Near its center rises the riverboat's smokestack. The pilothouse itself is a 12-foot by 15-foot enclosure with a ceiling 10 feet high. Glass windows ring the pilothouse entirely, giving an unobstructed view of the river during a voyage. Entry into the pilothouse is by means of a stairwell on the port side that leads up from the crew deck. There is also a door on the starboard side of the smokestack that leads out onto an observation deck.

Occupants: Normally, this room is empty, but in hazardous waters a watch may be set here. This crewman would be responsible for aiding the captain and steersman below.

CREW DECK

Description: Roughly 30 feet wide by 150 feet long, this deck is fronted by the wheel house, from which the boat is steered, and also the crew's cabins. The captain's cabin is rearmost, and looks out onto an open deck, where passengers may stroll or lounge about in the sun.

Occupants: During off-duty hours, the various crewmembers come here to sleep or for a little bit of privacy. The first mate's cabin is directly across from the water closet, and the chief steward's is just next door. The first mate and chief steward can be found in their cabins, sleeping, during the midnight to 6 a.m. shift. The captain normally spends that shift asleep in his own cabin as well, if it is necessary to find him. Occasionally he may entertain a guest or two in his cabin of an evening, and he may sometimes be found there during the noon to 6 p.m. shift, doing paperwork. During the 6 a.m. to noon shift, the captain is usually in the wheelhouse.

UPPER DECK

Description: Measuring roughly 50 feet wide by 175 feet long, this deck holds the smaller, less prestigious passenger cabins, none of which are in use during this particular voyage. The deck has a closed-in observation lounge both fore and aft, and a central balcony around the dining room below. The rooms just forward of the water closets are for storage of linens and the like.

Occupants: During this trip, this deck is unoccupied. Even the observation lounges see little use, given that the aft lounge and saloon on the deck below serve the boat's few passengers nicely. During the adventure, up the loneliness of this deck, its silence broken only occasionally by haunting echoes of the heroes' own footsteps.

MAIN DECK

Description: During this voyage, the passengers will spend most of their time on this deck. It measures by 50 feet wide by 200 feet long. The enclosed area holds a saloon at the forward end, a lounge at its aft end, and an impressive dining room at its center. The four doors opening into each side the saloon are lavish cabins, designed for more prestigious passengers. They are equipped with many amenities not included in the other cabins. The remainder of the rooms with outside entrances are standard passenger cabins. The large room opening into the starboard side of the dining area is the luxury suite. The large room opening into the dining room from the port side is the kitchen.

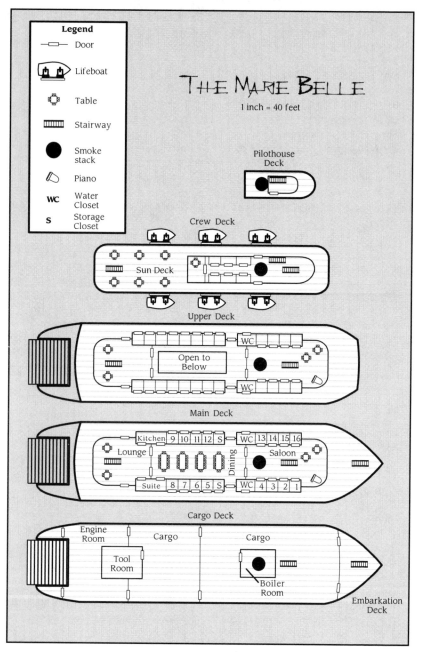

Legend

Door	
Lifeboat	
Table	
Stairway	
Smoke stack	
Piano	
WC	Water Closet
S	Storage Closet

THE MARIE BELLE

1 inch = 40 feet

Pilothouse Deck

Crew Deck

Sun Deck

Upper Deck

Open to Below

WC

WC

Main Deck

Kitchen | 9 | 10 | 11 | 12 | S

Lounge

WC | 13 | 14 | 15 | 16

Saloon

Dining

Suite | 8 | 7 | 6 | 5 | S

WC | 4 | 3 | 2 | 1

Cargo Deck

Engine Room

Cargo

Cargo

Tool Room

Boiler Room

Embarkation Deck

SKINNERS

Occupants: This deck sees most of the activity on this voyage. Not only does it hold the only occupied passenger cabins, but its aft lounge and forward saloon are popular spots, and (of course) the dining room serves as a common meeting spot.

THE CABIN ASSIGNMENTS

The passengers in this adventure are disposed as follows:

The Suite: Mrs. Adelia McPherson
Cabin 1: Detective Matthews
Cabin 2: Randall McPherson
Cabin 3: Rusty Carmichael
Cabin 4: Jack and Rita Baroni
Cabin 5: Alice Monroe
Cabin 6: Available for a member of the posse
Cabin 7: Available for a member of the posse
Cabin 8: Black Eagle.
Cabin 9: Available for a member of the posse
Cabin 10: Available for a member of the posse
Cabin 11: Available for a member of the posse
Cabin 12: Available for a member of the posse
Cabins 13: Available for a member of the posse
Cabin 14: Senator Milton Howard.
Cabin 15: Jefferson Andrews, the senator's aide.

CARGO DECK

Description: This deck is entirely enclosed, except at the very front of the deck, where the embarkation area is located. It measures roughly 50 feet across and nearly 240 feet long from stern to aft (including the wheel). The embarkation deck is roofed over, but open at the sides. A gangplank is extended from this area to the dock below with the ship is in port. Behind the embarkation deck is the forward cargo hold where most of the cargo is stored, with the boiler room located in its center. The next room back is the reserve cargo hold and storage area, with a tool room in the center of its rear wall. The engine room is furthest aft, and has doors leading to two uncovered walkways alongside the paddle wheel.

Occupants: One bosun is on duty in the boiler room at all times, and two engineers in the engine room. The holds are normally empty of personnel, and the embarkation deck is typically unoccupied during travel.

BOUNTY

Meeting most or all of the crew and passengers on board: 1 white chip.

CHAPTER TWO: THE BREAKFAST GATHERING

The first morning on the ship offers the heroes a chance to meet any of the passengers they may have missed during boarding. The crew has prepared a lavish breakfast for their guests, and everyone is in attendance. As the heroes enter the dining room they witness the following scene:

The dining room has an elegant glow in the soft light of brass lamps along the walls and slender white candles on the tables.

This long room is paneled in polished oak, with rich carpets on the floor, spotless linen spread throughout the room, and gleaming silver on six tables. The ceiling is roughly two stories high, with a gallery running around all four walls at half that height, opening onto the next deck up. As you enter, the chief steward smiles and nods in welcome, then turns back to talking with his assistant, as they prepare to serve the collected passengers.

The breakfast rolls are warm and flaky, the butter and preserves fresh, the coffee and tea hot and strong. The stewards are pleasant and friendly, and even the other passengers seem a bit sleepy and subdued at this early hour. The chief steward mentions that the portly gentleman sitting with the young man across the way is Senator Howard, an important CSA politician.

THE GRUESOME TWO-SOME

At this point in time, the villains are disguised as Alice Monroe and Jack Baroni (the male of the newlywed couple), victims they have killed for their riverboat tickets. Jack and Alice paid a higher price for their tickets than the others!

Alice's skinless remains were left in an abandoned warehouse. Her corpse won't be discovered for days, but Black Eagle has seen it.

Jack's remains were wrapped in a sheet, weighted with rocks, and dumped off the dock into the river. The skinners, cautious in their precarious situation, are just hoping that it won't be discovered until after the riverboat has moved on.

THE BREAKFAST PARTY

Besides the heroes, there are 11 other occupants enjoying the lavish breakfast spread in the dining room. Assuming there are roughly six heroes in the posse, the vessel is traveling with a total of only 15 passengers—only a quarter of the contingent that it's capable of carrying—and it has a lighter crew than usual.

Regardless of the number of passengers, the dining room is bustling with activity. Glancing over these people, the heroes may notice the following about the other occupants:

The chief steward and one of his assistants, dressed in black trousers and bright white serving jackets, are passing among the tables with trays of coffee and tea. They are serving each of the guests in turn. The other steward is filling water glasses for each person seated around the tables.

The senator and his aide are seated by themselves at one end of a table, laughing brightly at some shared joke.

MARSHAL: 45

SKINNERS

A young couple, possibly newlyweds, are sitting alone at one end of the first table, having a hushed row. Occasionally, she darts a glance at the woman in question, who is sitting at the far end of the next table over, all by herself. The young husband looks vaguely uncomfortable, but mainly bored.

(If any of the heroes think to pass close enough to them, they hear the young wife berating her husband in a fierce whisper, for having been caught talking with another young woman.)

The other young woman, wearing a fancy blue velvet dress, is lounging comfortably in her chair, and staring blatantly at the couple, a vaguely amused expression on her face. She seems to be enjoying the fiasco for which she is obviously to blame.

An American Indian dressed in a brown suit and derby is sitting at the farthest table, watching the crowd, with a slightly hostile air about him.

The obvious rustle of cards being shuffled draws your attention to a slick-looking fellow in a tight black suit with a ruffled shirt, velvet vest, and wide-brimmed black hat. He is perched at the opposite end of the same table where the Indian is seated.

Sitting at a table near the middle of the room is a woman in her mid-sixties dressed in gray brocaded silk and extensive jewelry, with deep frown lines marking her stoic face, She is seated with a still, pale-looking man in his thirties. The family resemblance between them is obvious.

Give the players a few minutes to roleplay the situation and get involved in the company of the other guests on board, then spring the events of the next section on them.

BOUNTY

Overhearing the young wife berating her husband about flirting with someone: 1 white chip.
Realizing that the young woman in blue velvet is the woman he spoke to: 1 white chip.

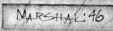

CHAPTER THREE: THE SKINLESS CORPSE

The breakfast is wonderful, but shortly after every one is situated and comfortable, the scene takes a turn for the worse.

As you sip at your cup and gaze around the elegant room, it strikes you that this should be a very comfortable trip, a welcome change from the normal pressures of your life–and those not-so-normal events that have drawn you into their clutches in the past. But banishing such thoughts, you relax and soak up the warmth of the setting, determined to take advantage of the time and place.

Then a ruckus begins outside on the dock. There is a man's startled cry of distress, followed by many shouting voices. After a quick word to his assistant, the chief steward leaves to investigate, a worried look on his face. Obviously, something unusual is occurring outside.

Wearing a polite smile, the junior steward passes among the tables again, offering more coffee and tea. Ignoring him, the senator rises and leaves as well, with his companion. Everyone else stares toward the dockside door.

ACT SURPRISED, DEAR

Once the hullabaloo begins, the skinners pretty much figure that it has to mean the discovery of Jack's body. All they can do now is try to keep a low profile and wait to see what happens, hoping that the voyage begins anyway.

THE HORRID DISCOVERY

Outside, on the dock, a cargo handler has discovered a hideous sight. He has pulled up the skinless remains of a human being, floating just under the dock. Drawn by his cry, other workers quickly gathered as well, and they have fished the body out with a loop of rope. The ship's captain arrives shortly, followed by the senator, and together they take charge of the situation until the New Orleans police can be summoned.

If any of the heroes wish to investigate the cries, the steward asks them to *please* remain in the dining room. He assures them that the ship's officers and the dock workers can handle any emergency that might have arisen, and that the passengers shouldn't concern themselves with the issue. Undoubtedly, he insists, all will be revealed shortly. He does not, however, attempt to physically restrain any passengers from leaving, though he will try to position himself between them and the dockside door if necessary, to politely discourage anyone from leaving.

Anyone watching the other passengers will—if they are subtle about it and make a successful Onerous (7) *scrutinize* roll—note that most of them look concerned and curious. Black Eagle looks tense, as if he wants to get up and leave. Jack Baroni is a bit fidgety as well, while Alice Monroe and Rusty Carmichael look studiously cool.

ONLY THE BLACK EAGLE KNOWS

Black Eagle is tense because he knows that the villains he's pursuing are aboard. The young husband looks tense because he hopes that his identity will not be discovered. The young woman looks cool because she is the brains behind the pair. The man in black looks cool because he's an experienced poker player.

On the dock, the heroes find a cluster of folks gathered around a skinless corpse— though everyone is trying not to look at it. Unless the heroes can show police credentials or pass a Hard (9) *persuasion* or *leadership* roll, none of them are allowed to examine the corpse. But it's obvious that the body is completely skinless, and that from its overall size, the victim must have been of average height and slender build. Each hero must make an Onerous (7) *Guts* check from the bloody sight.

If they can inspect the corpse, a successful Onerous (7) *search* or a Fair (5) *medicine: general* roll reveals the throat has been cut, and that despite the body's recent immersion in the water, it is still oozing blood. From this last fact and the limpness of the limbs and lack of decomposition, a Fair (5) *medicine: general* roll makes it clear that the victim was killed very recently, most likely this morning.

Within a relatively few minutes of when the messenger was sent for them, the first police arrive on the scene. Immediately upon viewing the body, they cordon off the area and send for an ambulance and a detective. They also forbid the launching of the *Marie Belle*. If the heroes have not joined the crowd on the docks, the chief steward soon returns to announce this delay to the passengers.

The Uh-Oh Squad

When the Detective Brian Matthews arrives, he spends some time studying the body before allowing it to be carted away, then carefully examines the dock and its environs, before turning his attention to the witnesses. This physical examination takes roughly half an hour, by the end of which time the sun is rising above everyone's head.

Next, he boards the boat and checks the passenger and crew rosters, then asks to see everyone's tickets, all total the work of another half an hour. The end result of this head counting is that he learns everyone on the roster is aboard; there is no one missing, and no one extra.

Stymied for the moment, Matthews announces that the *Marie Belle's* voyage will have to be delayed until this murder has been solved.

Hearing this, the senator throws a grand fit. Red-faced and shouting, he insists that he has important governmental business waiting in St. Louis.

In response, Matthews sends a runner back to police headquarters with a report of the situation. An hour later, word comes back the detective is to accompany the boat to Memphis, questioning the passengers along the way.

Sourly, Matthews receives these orders, then accompanies the Chief Steward to be assigned a stateroom and receive the loan of some extra clothing.

Roughly two and a half hours late, the *Marie Belle* finally begins its voyage.

Bounty

Noticing the Indian's tension: 1 white chip.
Managing to view the skinless body: 1 red chip.

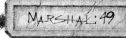

CHAPTER FOUR: THE QUESTIONING

With the *Marie Belle* finally under steam, the heroes will have plenty of free time on their hands. The murder is still fresh on everyone's mind, and the Marshal should read this to the posse:

> Up on deck, leaning against the polished brass railing to peer across the river's calm surface to a wooded shore beneath an achingly blue sky, you reflect that this trip would be a perfect time to rest and recuperate your weary soul—were it not for the ugly specter of the hideous murder back in New Orleans.
>
> As if on cue with your thoughts, Detective Matthews appears, escorting Miss Monroe. The two talk a moment more; Matthews jots down a final note, then tips his hat to the young lady, who saunters off. Gazing about, the detective settles his eyes on you and strides purposefully your way. Apparently, it is your turn to be questioned.

UNDER PRESSURE

This can be a perfect point at which to make the posse sweat a bit, if they are like most heroes and have an unusual number of weapons secreted about their person, or strange items hidden in their baggage.

AVOIDING SUSPICION

The one goal the skinners have at this time is simply to keep the finger of suspicion from pointing their way. To this end, "Jack" talks his young wife Rita into providing him with an alibi for his time off the boat this morning. Unfortunately, Rita is not a very convincing liar. (See **Conversations Overheard**, below.)

SETTLING IN

To prepare for this part of the adventure, have the players take a moment to discuss where their characters would likely be on the boat through this first day of the voyage. Some might be strolling about one of the decks, others might be reading, smoking, or playing cards in one or another of the lounges, others still might be resting in their staterooms, or even pursuing an investigation of their own concerning the grisly murder. Just let them mill about the boat, exploring and settling in for the trip.

Once the players have each imagined a setting for his character, play through Matthews stopping each of them in turn and questioning them about what they might know that could help him in solving this murder. The detective asks if he can search their rooms for clues, and he turns a suspicious eye on anyone who refuses.

If the detective notices much weaponry about a hero, or strange items among that character's belongings, he is certain to prod about them. Sample sarcastic comments he might make include: "So, are you expecting a war to break out?" or "Well, we're certainly armed for bear, aren't we?" or "By the looks of all this, you must be the high priest of some long-forgotten god," or even, "Don't you think all this is just a bit much?" In playing Matthews, do your best to put the heroes on the defensive, and to make them think he will be watching them closely.

CONVERSATIONS OVERHEARD

As Matthews questions the other people aboard ship, the posse members may attempt to overhear the conversations, or maybe conduct their own investigations. Matthews will tolerate a little interference, but not much.

Matthews conducts a fairly thorough investigation of everyone on board. A summary of each is listed below.

CAPTAIN MANNING

The captain informs the detective that he was running a last inspection aboard ship through the hours that the murder must have taken place. The crew can verify this if Matthews pursues the issue.

ABLE SIMMS

Like the captain, Simms was working aboard ship from midnight on, and other crewmen can attest to the fact if necessary.

ASSISTANT STEWARDS

One spent most of his time with the Chief Steward, Able Simms, all save the last hour when he stood at the gangplank to collect tickets. The other was sleeping in his cabin throughout those hours, although no one can testify on his behalf.

SHIP'S HANDS

Two engineers and two bosuns were working through the hours from midnight to 6 a.m.; the other four crew were sleeping. It would have been even more difficult for one of these crewmen to leave the ship without being seen than it would have been for the second assistant steward to have done so.

SENATOR HOWARD AND HIS AIDE

These two didn't arrive on board until just before breakfast. They came here directly from their hotel.

JACK AND RITA BARON

These newlyweds say that they arrived aboard ship last night, and that they went directly to their cabin, where they were "indisposed" until just before breakfast. But Rita acts strangely evasive in telling this tale. She is covering for her husband.

In reality, while the two arrived when they say, they had an argument immediately thereafter and Jack left the cabin to go fume on the dock. The skinners caught him on the dock, and Emerson took his place, slipping aboard while Janice (disguised as Alice) distracted the steward.

Any of the posse members that make an Onerous (7) *scrutinize* roll detect Rita's discomfort. The detective, noting her uneasiness, puts it down to embarrassment at being questioned about the private time with her husband.

ADELIA MCPHERSON AND SON

Mrs. McPherson dismisses the detective's questions imperiously with the line, "Surely you can't suspect *me* of this crime, nor my boy!" When she is pressed, Randall interjects a quiet statement that they left their hotel late and only just arrived in time for breakfast.

"RUSTY" CARMICHAEL

Carmichael arrived at the boat at midnight, and fast-talked his way aboard despite the late hour. He spent four hours in his cabin, then went to the rear lounge, where he sat shuffling cards and smoking cigars until breakfast. Many of the crewmembers saw him there during that time.

Alice Monroe

Alice Monroe is actually Janice Humphries in Alice's skin, and this young lady claims to have spent the morning packing her many pieces of luggage (and they *are* extensive, which the ticket-taking steward is ready to attest). Of course, she really arrived on the dock early, with her partner Emerson Walker, where they lurked about among the stacks of off-loaded cargo, waiting for someone they could waylay for his ticket and skin.

"Tom" Black Eagle

Black Eagle arrived in town just in time to purchase a ticket for the voyage from the steward at the gangplank. The steward was struck both by his determination to get aboard and the amount of money he flashed to accomplish that. When questioned, Black Eagle pretends to understand very little English.

Bounty

For any passenger conversations heard (or overheard): 1 white chip (limit of 1).
Conducting a good investigation of their own: 1 red chip.
Managing to gain Detective Matthews' trust: 1 red chip.

Chapter Five: Scorched Bones

As the posse digs into the mystery, it continues to grow deeper by the moment. The *Marie Belle* continues on its voyage as yet another gruesome discovery is made.

Despite the darkly auspicious launching of this voyage, you sleep soundly through the first night. All too early the next morning, however, a distraught steward passes from cabin to cabin, asking everyone to assemble in the dining room. When you arrive, it is to find the captain and Matthews waiting for everyone.

After everyone arrives, Matthews makes a grim announcement: "The killer is definitely aboard with us, folks. We have found two more bodies, this time just scorched bones in the boiler room's firebox."

A quick head count reveals the two missing people to be Alice Monroe and one of the ship's engineers.

3

CRISPY CRITTERS

Worried at Rita's botched attempt at covering for her "husband," the skinners have killed the young wife, and Janice has taken her place. In order to dispose of the remains, they decided to burn them in the ship's firebox.

The skinners accomplished all this by plying the engineer with whiskey, then promising him a sexual romp in the boiler room with him, "Alice," "Jack," and Rita in attendance.

"Jack" chloroformed Rita and carried her to the boiler room, where "Alice" joined them. Together, they overpowered the engineer, skinned him and Rita, and burned the bodies.

Unfortunately, an observant ship's pilot and a less-than-perfect mopping job bring the murders to light, as explained below.

SHOCKING NEWS

Reactions to the news of the murders varies. Most people seem shocked. Senator Howard seems angry instead, as does Black Eagle. "Rusty" Carmichael seems vaguely amused; it is obvious that he has been drinking. Jack Baroni stares blankly ahead, steely eyed, patting Rita's hand. For her part, Rita shivers once at the news, then clutches Jack's arm, dropping her gaze to hide a slight smile.

Matthews goes on to say that until the boat reaches Memphis, the passengers should stay locked in their cabin as much as possible, not letting anyone else in. Once the boat docks at Memphis, the voyage will be halted until the mystery can be solved and the killer put behind bars. Read the following to the players:

> At this news, Senator Howard stands and shouts, "Now see here, Matthews! We've had this discussion before, and I simply won't abide with this voyage being delayed. I have important business to attend to in St. Louis."
>
> Matthews replies tersely, "If your business were that important, senator, you should have taken the train."
>
> The senator blusters, "Why you impertinent little...!"
>
> The captain interrupts him, calmly but firmly. "I'm afraid it isn't your decision, Senator. Aboard ship, it's mine."
>
> After a silent staring match with the captain, Senator Howard looks away, says, "Come, Jefferson," and stalks out, his aide following.

Digging Deeper

The heroes learn that the pilot noticed a drop-off in power just after 3 a.m., and when the engineer failed to answer the ship's telegraph, he took the wheel and sent the bosun to investigate.

Finding no one attending the boiler, the bosun began to look around. After several minutes of fruitless search, he remembered the odd fact that the boiler room floor had been freshly mopped.

Checking again, he found traces of blood in one corner of the room. He woke the captain, who dug among the coals in the firebox and came up with pieces of two skulls, plus many other bones.

A little bit of deductive reasoning gives the captain an idea of who the victims are. Considering that the engineer and Miss Monroe are missing, it seems likely that it is their bones among the ashes.

If the posse members mention to the detective that the Baronis had been arguing over Alice Monroe, he thanks the heroes and says he'll watch the pair for a bit, then question them closely. In the meantime, he asks the heroes to keep an eye on the senator, his aide, the Indian, and the gambler, though he warns them to be surreptitious and careful around those suspects.

Another Odd Occurrence

At some point during the night, the skinners find Matthews and take his skin. If the posse is watching the pair too closely for this to occur—despite the general admonition that everyone remained locked in their quarters, and the posse's assignment to watch the senator, his aide, the Indian, and the gambler—arrange for some distraction to take them away from the Baronis' door. Black Eagle might confront the senator, for example, precipitating a shouting match.

If nothing else works, use the skinners themselves to confuse the posse. Emerson might leave the room in a different skin, for example, carrying a bag with Jack's clothes and skin inside. The posse should be astonished to find this stranger aboard the vessel, the more so when he loses them for a few minutes in some dark spot or another and Jack appears coming back that way.

Either bit of deception can give Janice time to switch from Rita's skin to Alice's for a visit to the detective. Matthews will, of course, be astonished to find Alice still alive, and will happily accompany her back to her quarters to talk. The plan is for Emerson to be waiting for them there, ready to help kill the detective and take his place. They dispose of his skinless body by dumping it in pieces down the nearest toilet.

If you really want to confuse the Posse, let them happen along just as "Rita" and "Matthews" exit the wash closet together and sneak back to the newlyweds' room.

BOUNTY POINTS

Learning the details of the pair's death: 1 red chip.
Mentioning that the Baronis quarreled over Alice Monroe earlier: 1 white chip.

CHAPTER SIX: THE VILLAIN EXPIRES

As the *Marie Belle* presses on, the mood among the passengers is somber, and Detective Matthews is still conducting his investigation.

The next morning, when everyone assembles for breakfast, Matthews makes a surprise announcement that he has changed his mind about holding the ship at Memphis. He says that he feels confident that the case is nearly solved, and that no more deaths will occur.

Senator Howard is clearly pleased by this news.

DESPERATE MEASURES

Forced to take matters into their own hands if they wanted to keep the voyage from being halted, the skinners killed Matthews. Emerson is playing the part of "Matthews," while Janice remains in her role as "Rita," in order to cover for "Jack's" absence.

The strain of multiple roles is beginning to tell.

MUSTO '99

MISSING PIECES AND PASSENGERS

If the heroes take note of who has come for breakfast, they find that the off-duty crew members are present, as well as the pilot (who says the captain is taking a watch in the wheel house). All of the passengers are present except for Jack Baroni.

If asked, Rita says that he is tired and wanted to sleep late. Detective Matthews offers to go check on him, and though Rita acts hesitant for a moment, then she nods her approval and thanks the detective.

Minutes later, Jack comes to the dining room, saying that Matthews told him people were asking about his health. He claims that after waking him, the detective said he was going to talk with the captain.

WATCHING THE DETECTIVE

If any of the posse seek out the detective, they find him later in the day. If they press him for more explanation of his reasons for not holding the boat at Memphis, he does one of two things, depending upon how many of the heroes talk to him at once.

THE POSSE CONFRONTS THE DETECTIVE

If more than one hero confronts Detective Matthews, he tries to get all but one of them to do him a "valuable favor" and go check up on his "prime suspects": the senator, his aide, the Indian, and the gambler. If this succeeds, he takes the lone remaining hero aside.

If the heroes won't split up as he asks, but keep pressing him, he resorts to simply standing upon his authority, claiming that to reveal anything of his reasons to them now might alert the real killer, who might then strike again or even escape. If the heroes continue to pressure him further, he tries to leave their presence. Ultimately, if they simply won't let him go, he panics and runs.

A HERO CONFRONTS THE DETECTIVE

If only one hero asks to talk with Matthews, or if he manages to split up the posse as above, Detective Matthews (Emerson) invites the lone hero to meet with him in his cabin in 10 minutes, where he tries to chloroform the cowpoke. For combat, remember to use the stats for Emerson Walker, listed at the beginning of the adventure.

Once combat ensues, if the skinner overpowers the hero, he skins the victim with the ritual dagger, and either he or Janice (depending upon the sex) will wear the skin, using the new guise to lure other heroes to their doom as well, one at a time. As each new posse member is killed, take the unfortunate player aside and explain the situation (her demise at the hands of the killers) to her.

Ask the player to continue to act out her hero, but with the understanding that the character is dead and being impersonated by a skinner. This is a golden opportunity for some good roleplaying, as the player must portray someone else trying to be their hero!

RUN AWAY!

If, during any combat with a posse member, the hero seems likely to win the battle, or if someone comes to the hero's aid (if he or she was canny enough to ask someone else to lurk nearby in case of trouble, for instance), the skinner flees and jumps overboard, hoping to swim for shore.

Most likely, this will occur when Emerson attacks the very first hero, or if he cannot get a hero alone and they all continue to press him for an explanation.

Unfortunately, diving into the river proves to be a fatal mistake. Once immersed in running water, the skinner discovers to his horror that the borrowed skin comes loose!

The heroes see him dive into the water, dog paddle for a moment to get his bearings on the nearest shore, and then begin floundering about as his skin sags in huge wrinkles. Within seconds, a seam develops, and the skin begins slipping off of him in one huge piece, beginning with his head, and proceeding downward.

His skin slowly slides out of the neck of his clothing, leaving him a fleshless, bleeding thing that quickly sinks, as he screams in horror and pain. After a few moments of spashing white water and foamy bubbles, the commotion stops and the river continues on. He has drowned. The skin floats eerily atop the water for a moment, then sinks as well.

Each hero that sees the horrible scene should make a Hard (9) *guts* check. For the moment, though, let them think their heroes have defeated the villain.

Bounty

Viewing the skinner's demise: 1 white chip.
Finding out Emerson may be the murderer before his death: 1 red chip.

Chapter Seven: One Down...

The following text assumes that Emerson died in the guise of the detective. If he died in the guise of a posse member, or if Janice died instead, modify the following text to account for the change.

> *Everyone aboard the* Marie Belle *is shocked at the detective's death. While Matthews' attack on one of your friends, and his subsequent flight and death, certainly point to his guilt as the murderer, the manner of his passing remains inexplicable. Captain Manning suggests that the cause of death must have been piranhas, or some other flesh-eating fish, and Senator Howard mumbles a stunned agreement. (Of course, everyone knows that such things are not native to the Mississippi!) Black Eagle says it was the punishment of the Great Spirit.*
>
> *In any case, it would seem that the horror is behind you now, and all that remains is to complete the voyage.*

The Last of the Skinners

Janice is in something of a panic at the loss of Emerson. While she has certainly been the leader of the pair, without his help she cannot hope to continue playing the roles of all their victims so far.

Consequently, she decides to abandon the guise of Rita Baroni, and take on the guise of the Senator (who was killed the night before, along with his aide as they were smoking on the deck). This way she can easily explain away the disappearance of Rita, Jack, and the senator's aide.

Donning Senator Howard's skin (which is no easy feat, mind you), she sets the rest of her devilish plan in motion.

She's a Man, Baby!

In order to disguise herself as the senator, who (needless to say) was quite portly, Janice has had to pad out her body with thick slabs of the senator's fat! Prior to donning the skin, she used strips of linen torn from bed sheets to bind slabs of the senator's body fat to her skinless torso and limbs. Consequently, her disguise is less than perfect, with pinched places in the flesh evident under close examination. In addition, Janice is a few inches shorter than the senator, which means that his skin hangs loosely in places, and she prefers to be seen seated, because then the discrepancy in height is not evident.

It's Not Over Yet!

If the players believe that the problem is now solved, let them enjoy that feeling for a bit. Take some time to describe the scenery passing by on either shore, the passing of the locks at Beardstown, and a sumptuous dinner that evening. Make it seem as if you are winding down the adventure—then spring the next development on them.

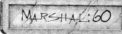

Senator Howard leaves the dinner a few minutes early, ostensibly to have a cigar in the fresh air. Black Eagle takes this as an excuse to leave as well.

Just moments later, the senator comes running back into the dining room, in an apparent panic, shouting that his aide just got in a fight with Jack Baroni, and that when Rita tried to separate them, all three fell over the side into the river.

When the heroes follow the senator back out to the railing, they catch just a glimpse of two more skins floating loose upon the water, shortly to sink thereafter.

"Piranhas? Again?" the senator asks, in a stunned whisper.

GRIM REVELATIONS

In the meantime, one of the bosuns finds Black Eagle searching the newlyweds' stateroom. When taken before the captain, Black Eagle breaks down and begins babbling that there is a "skinwalker" loose on the boat, and that it must not be allowed to escape.

The captain responds to this chaos by having Black Eagle locked up in his quarters until this apparent madman can be questioned more closely.

Convinced that he has no other option, and having learned that skinwalkers cannot swim, Black Eagle starts a fire in his room, hoping that it will spread to the rest of the boat. When crewmen come to put the fire out, he barricades the door to keep them out, despite the fact that this means he will perish in the conflagration. Black Eagle considers it his sacred duty to destroy the skinner, even though it means his own doom as well.

A CAGED ANIMAL!

This puts Janice in perilous position. Having seen Emerson's horrible drowning, she knows that she cannot swim to shore. But she can don one of the animal pelts that she and Emerson stole along with the dagger—an eagle's skin, in this case—and fly away. The trouble is, she needs privacy to make the change, but if she does so in a closed room, in eagle form she cannot open the door to escape.

Taking advantage of the chaos of the burning ship, then, she recovers the dagger and bundle of pelts from where she has stowed them in the senator's quarters, and then heads for the steering room. Once there, she clubs the bosun at the wheel, locks the doors, and begins doffing the senator's skin, in full view of anyone watching outside through the steering room's large windows. Her desperate attempt to escape overshadows her desire to remain anonymous.

Be sure to play up the gruesome horror of this spectacle. First, Janice tears open the senator's clothing; then she splits open his skin. As the skin sloughs off, the slabs of bloody fat that she has bound to her body for padding become clearly visible against her naked musculature.

Just before donning the eagle skin, she smashes open one of the windows with her skinless elbow—making a bloody splotch on it with her first try, then shattering it with her second, harder blow. Finally, she transforms into a huge eagle and launches into the air, carrying the bundle of pelts with the dagger inside.

WELL, WHAT NOW?

Of course, the posse needn't just let her do all of this unopposed. What they do to stop her depends upon when they notice the "senator's" activities. Even after her change, they might be able to down her with a well-placed shot. Whatever their choice, there's sure to be a fight.

AFTERMATH

If Black Eagle ends up burning the riverboat, most of the passengers and crew manage to swim to shore. From there, once day breaks, it is the walk of only several hours, at most, to the last town down river. The only people who do not make it to shore alive are Mrs. McPherson (who is simply too old to survive being dumped in the water), "Rusty" Carmichael (who suffers a fatal heart attack from the exertion of swimming), and Black Eagle (who perishes in the fire).

If the heroes manage to detect and thwart Janice *before* Black Eagle is locked in his quarters, they may be able to prevent the fire. In that case, the riverboat halts at Memphis for the investigation.

Of course, there isn't much evidence for the Memphis police to work from—unless the posse has taken the dagger and roll of pelts and show it to them, which isn't likely. Assuming that no evidence is presented beyond the bones rescued from the firebox, the police rule the case closed, considering that the one demonstrable murderer (Emerson, disguised as the detective) drowned.

The other victims are filed as missing or drowned. Any mention of supernatural events is politely disregarded as hysterics.

Of course, rumors will spread about this cursed voyage, and among those who believe such things, the heroes could find themselves with something of a reputation.

BOUNTY

Capturing the skinning knife: 1 red chip
Preventing Black Eagle from burning the *Marie Belle*: 1 red chip
Stopping Janice from escaping: 1 blue chip

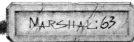

Don't Get Caught In The Same Old Web

Pinnacle Entertainment Group invites you to check out our Weird Website™ devoted to Deadlands™: The Weird West™, Deadlands: The Great Rail Wars™, and Deadlands: Hell on Earth™. We've crammed the site with sticky strands of tasty tidbits sure to please that ornery imagination, and we update the site regularly. So come on by and visit for a spell, or two, or three...

www.peginc.com

THE WEIRD WEST™

ORIGINS AWARD WINNER
The Year's Best Games

HELL ON EARTH™
The Wasted West Roleplaying Game

THE GREAT RAIL WARS™
MINIATURES BATTLE GAME

ORIGINS AWARD WINNER
The Year's Best Games

PINNACLE™